A Place To Be

The Inspirational Story of

Martin House
children's hospice

Edited by
Jan Aldridge

Printed by Wigley Print Services and
Silprint Ltd., U.K.

First published in Great Britain in 2008
by
Martin House
Grove Road
Clifford, Wetherby
Yorkshire, UK, LS23 6TX

Online ordering facility. Direct sales to anywhere in the world.
www.martinhouse.org.uk/shop/othersales

British Library Cataloguing – in – Publication Data
A catalogue record for this book is available from the British Library

ISBN 978-0-9561236-0-2

Printed and bound by Wigley Print Services and
Silprint Ltd, Yorkshire, UK

Martin House is
A Company Limited by Guarantee Registration No. 2016332, England & Wales
Registered Charity No. 517919
VAT Registration No. 686 5694 67

contents

Foreword: Ted Bowman

Section one: early days

Section two: philosophy

Section three: stories from martin house

Section four: developments

Section five: new perspectives

Section six: a rich tapestry

A whObOdy PlQce

Once upon a time, I discovered a book, now regrettably out of print. It was the story of the difference between anybodies and whobodies. Whobodies, I read, are different, especially for children, because whobodies are real, honest, fun, and want to be with children. Anybodies tolerate children – at times – but clearly have other, more important to them, things on their mind than children. Children know the difference between anybodies and whobodies.

It was many years after reading the book that I met many whobodies who work at a whobody place. It is called Martin House Children's Hospice. I was not sick when I stayed at Martin House (three times), but I was clearly better when I left. And, unknown to the staff, I took just a little bit of the special air and spirit with me when I left. I have been planting Martin House Whobody Seeds all over the world.

Now, picture a group of children who are invited to imagine the best of places to be IF, really IF, you happened to be SICK, really SICK. Many suggestions are put on a list: favourite places like mountaintops, forests or seashores; places where you could play, even if ill; a place where your friends could come. That it had to be a place of fun as well as where good care is provided comes up again and again. Laughter and tears are to be allowed and encouraged. And not all the carers would be old people! The children could care for each other too.

For anyone who has ever visited, stayed at, or worked in Martin House or Whitby Lodge, imagining such a conversation is not at all difficult. Somebodies, beginning with whobody Lenore Hill, started this conversation over 20 years ago and, lo and behold, the conversation goes on. It is a never-ending topic when quality care for children and families is the only choice.

Martin House is that rare place that embodies a match between environment and staff, between what is said and what is done, between what is in the mission statement and what occurs everyday, between the original dream and the emerging vision. Martin House is more than a place; it is more than its staff. It is a Whobody Place.

In the following pages, you will read about the phenomenal history and evolving story of Martin House. Read it with the knowledge that there are few places like it. Read it with the desire that you might take something from the pages that you can also share, as I have done, in other places. Yes, some illnesses are contagious. So is hope, authenticity, teamwork, and living as fully as you possibly can. Martin House knows that.

Ted Bowman is an educator about grief and loss and about hope. He has worked several times with the staff of Martin House and Whitby Lodge. He lives in Saint Paul, Minnesota, USA.

© Bindy Pease

Introduction and overview

It was late one winter's evening in Whitby Lodge, the teenage and young adult part of Martin House. Twenty-one year old J-P was having one of his signature trademark, thought-provoking and challenging conversations with Cath, one of the care team and me. It was then, as he lay in his bed, breathing with the aid of his ventilator, unable to feed himself, unable to sit up on his own, that he said with his impish smile, twinkling eyes and infectious good humour, 'Life is amazing…You just have to trust and follow your dreams.' Coming from him, these words make you listen.

J-P was born in 1987 with a life-shortening illness, the same year as Martin House came into being. His illness meant that many people thought he would never reach adulthood, and he has certainly had more than his fair share of admissions to intensive care units and a number of near death experiences, but he celebrated his 21st birthday in 2008. He has so many plans for the future, and for sharing his hard earned lessons and his dreams with others. This means that he has to work hard to squeeze in his regular restorative visits to Martin House.

Section 1: The early days

Similar strong and visionary qualities must have been right there in the founding mothers and fathers of Martin House when it too came into being in 1987. There was only one other established children's hospice in the world when Richard Seed moved from his parish in Oxford to one in Boston Spa in Yorkshire. In Oxford, Helen House had recently come into being through Helen, her parents and Sister Frances Dominica. Richard had seen at first hand how very valuable a second children's hospice would be in the north of the UK, and by one of those fortuitous coincidences the senior Consultant Paediatric Oncologist in Leeds at the time, Cliff Bailey, was actively exploring this very concept. It so came about that in May 1982 Cliff and some of the Leeds based paediatricians approached Richard to bring together a team of people to build a hospice for children. There followed a competition for an architect. As soon as he heard about it Michael Wildblood just knew he was the man for the job. He was the one responsible for the concept of a harbour, a place where families could come for shelter and to reprovision. In Chapters Two, Three and Four they tell the story in their own words.

Lenore Hill, the founding Head Nurse of Martin House, picks up the baton in Chapter Five. She was appointed in 1986, twelve months before the building opened. This meant that not only could she start straight away providing care for children in their own homes, but that her vision could be woven into the fabric of the building and the philosophy of Martin House right from the start. She did not want a place where children just came when they were very ill, rather somewhere they felt they could be themselves throughout the course of their illness - a place that was a resource for the families and supported them, without taking over. Lenore also talks about the involvement of the Sisters of the Holy Paraclete, who from the beginning have helped Martin House tend to the needs of the whole person: body, mind and spirit.

Section 2: The Philosophy of Martin House

Since these beginnings Martin House has grown considerably and, heavily guided by the families, it has been able to develop and expand what it is able to offer. However, the care, values and central philosophy at the heart of Martin House remain very much the same. This philosophy is described in Chapter Six by Jenny Wilkinson, a founding parent and now Trustee, and Sheila O'Leary, Martin House's second Head of Care who took over from Lenore Hill upon her retirement in 2004.

Section 3: Stories from Martin House

In this section we see how the guiding philosophy behind Martin House translates into practice. Bob Drought, a member of the care team, guides us through a day in the life of Martin House in Chapter Seven. In Chapter Eight members of the care team, parents and children provide insights into their adventures, day to day happenings and special understandings.

Chapters Seven and Eight show just how much flexibility there is on a day to day basis in what happens at Martin House. Children and families can have quiet, peaceful times or very active days together or apart, depending on what each individual child and family wants. Music and art can make important contributions to these days if the children wish, maybe mirroring their mood and providing alternative ways of relating. Helen Scouller and Sarah Aspinall give a flavour of their work as artists in residence in Chapter Nine, and Mike Gilroy gives an insight into his work, together with that of the other music therapists and musicians, Cathy Ibberson and Caroline Illingworth, in Chapter Ten.

The last chapter in this section is again written by Bob Drought. Children becoming very ill and dying is part of Martin House - Bob guides us through one such experience. In Chapter Eleven he writes about saying goodbye and a child's funeral.

Section 4: Developments

Martin House's development might be described as organic. It has gently grown and evolved with the many changes it has seen over the years, but it has also remained true to its core philosophy, with people and human relationships at its centre. Some of these developments are described in Chapters Twelve to Sixteen.

© Bindy Pease

One such important development during the first 10 years was the flexible extension of care into the children's own homes. This happened with the setting up of the Community Team in 1997. The flexibility and resourcefulness of this team ensures that it is a popular and well used service. In 2007 it expanded further, with the appointment of a part-time nursery nurse. She works particularly with the brothers and sisters of the ill children at home. Sheila O'Leary explores the varied work of the Community team in Chapter Twelve.

Supporting families - whether at home or in Martin House - whilst their child is ill is obviously crucial. Martin House knew early on just how important it was for families to have the option of this support continuing after their child had died. Linda Hedley, one of the three Deputy Heads of Care, with a particular responsibility for the bereavement team who work with parents and grandparents, talks about what bereavement support Martin House offers in Chapter Thirteen.

From the beginning Hazel Clough, the first Deputy Head of Care, has been very aware of the needs of the brothers and sisters of the ill child. In Chapter Fourteen she talks about these needs and the support Martin House has developed specifically for them over the last sixteen years.

A major development in the first 21 years has been the provision of Whitby Lodge for teenagers and young adults. Set next to Martin House, within the same beautiful grounds, Whitby Lodge opened its doors to young people in 2001 and

© Bindy Pease

since then it has gone from strength to strength. It was the first hospice of its kind in the world and Hazel Clough, who has special responsibility for Whitby Lodge, explains how it came into being and what it offers in Chapter Fifteen.

The final chapter in this section explores the essential place of education and training in Martin House.

With expansion of the care team, the administrative team, fund-raising and the essential volunteer base, education and training needs have also grown. The skills needed to deliver the best possible care are continually developing and this has had considerable implications for staff training. Another challenge for Martin House in providing optimal care for children with life-limiting illnesses and their families is informing and educating outside health care professionals. In 2000, one of the Deputy Heads of Care, Linda Foley, was appointed as Head of Education and she provides an insight into her continually expanding role in Chapter Sixteen.

section 5: New perspectives

A question that many organisations must face at some time in their development is how to keep growing and responding to changing needs without losing the essence of who they are? Martin House is no different. In particular, how does it keep its holistic, flexible way of working, where each member of the care team will provide many aspects of a child and family's care, and yet also avail itself of the latest medical and psychological advances?

True to its spirit of providing the best for its children, families and staff, Martin House put in a bid for national development money to appoint a Consultant in Paediatric Palliative Care and a Consultant Clinical Psychologist. They were successful in their bid and the two new appointments were made in 2004. You can read how Dr Mike Miller and Dr Jan Aldridge have developed these posts in medicine and clinical psychology in Chapters 17 and 18 respectively.

section 6: A rich tapestry

Martin House is blessed to have an exceptional team. This is made up not only of frontline carers, but also multi-talented administrators, fundraisers and volunteers. Representatives from the administrative team of staff and volunteers describe something of their varied roles in Chapter 19. In the same chapter Stuart Andrew, Fundraising Manager together with members of his team give an insight into the varied ways in which individuals and organisations support Martin House and make its work possible.

Martin House is like a richly coloured tapestry, with many different threads woven together to produce one beautiful whole. It is not possible to unpick them all and examine each separately without much being lost in the unpicking. The resident chef, Robin, is one such nurturing thread. I could not persuade him to leave his kitchen long enough to write a chapter, but he gave me one of his favourite recipes for Chapter 20. This sits alongside a recipe for a favourite chocolate cake from one of his dedicated kitchen volunteers, Carol Spratt.

The ever attentive, infinitely patient and resourceful housekeepers, Olive, Angie, Dot, and Lynda are other examples of the threads in the tapestry. Olive has produced one of her infamous drawings of them for the same chapter. The two maintenance men, Pete and Peter, also do a lot of looking after and nurturing, taking care of so much inside Martin House, and in the gardens. The gardens are a source of great pleasure in so many different ways and Gillian writes about her role as head volunteer gardener in the same chapter.

From the beginning, with the support of the nuns from the Order of the Holy Paraclete, the concept of chaplaincy has been an important thread in the tapestry. Mark Clayton has continued to develop and enrich this with his links with a range of communities and faiths in his work as chaplain at Martin House. He describes something of his varied role in our final chapter (Chapter Twenty-one).

I hope you enjoy this inspirational book - enjoy dipping into the various chapters and reading the related stories at the ends of the chapters. I hope the variety and the diverse contributions from the broad family of people who make up Martin House give a sense of, 'this place to be.'

© Bindy Pease

15

Section One:
Early Days

As one of the world's first children's hospices Martin House helped define the concept and their very way of working. They were not to become junior versions of adult hospices, places focused on caring for individuals in the final stages of their lives. Rather they were to be organisations that would work with, and advocate for, children with life threatening illnesses or potentially life-shortening conditions, and their families all along the way-whatever that way would be.

How the dream of Martin House came about is described by the founders, Professor Cliff Bailey, The Venerable Richard Seed Archdeacon of York, Architect Michael Wildblood and first Head Nurse Lenore Hill in the four chapters in this section. There are also vivid memories and contributions from some of the care team who were part of those early days and continue to be part of Martin House today.

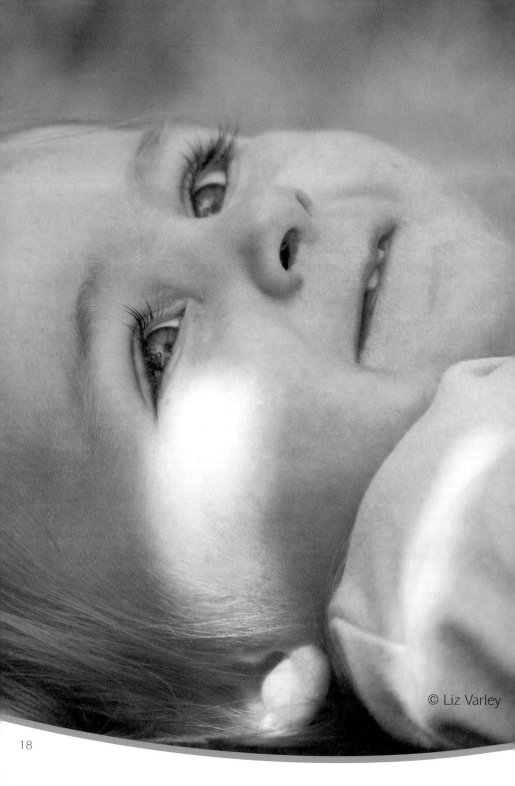

© Liz Varley

18

The team is born

The beginnings

One morning I received a telephone call from a public health consultant in Sheffield who asked if I was interested in the idea of a hospice for children. He had heard of the work of Sister Frances in Oxford and wondered if we should have such a facility in the north of England.

 At that time I was developing a busy regional service caring for children with cancer. We had a small team providing liaison between the hospital and the child's locally based medical, nursing and educational teams because we saw the importance of maintaining the linkages into the child's local community throughout their period of illness. We also were committed to the concept of provision of terminal care in the child's own home by supporting the family and the local medical services with our own staff to enable this care to take place. We had found that with this support and the support of their extended family many families could be helped through the extreme trauma of the loss of their child. On occasion we had worked with adult hospices to care for children. However, whilst the staff in the adult units did their best we regularly received feedback that they felt that they were inadequately trained to provide the care needed by children and their families. Adult hospices at that time were seen as providing only a hospice based terminal care service as opposed to the extended services now seen and this was widely thought to be inappropriate for children. Some families however needed the support of the hospital and for them we provided an open door access. I therefore told my Sheffield colleague that I thought that we were providing most of what was needed and a hospice was not necessary.

Fortunately I was responsible for organising a series of postgraduate lectures and it seemed a good idea to hear more about what was going on in Oxford and so I invited Sister Frances to come and speak to the Leeds paediatricians. She opened my eyes to the fact that I had been thinking in too narrow a fashion. What we provided for children with cancer was fine but similar provision was not available to children with a whole range of other life threatening diseases and in addition a children's hospice could provide important periods of respite care which might enable a family to recharge its strength and continue to provide care in their own home.

After her lecture Professor Richard Smithills, Dr. John Buckler and I met and resolved to do something to provide a Helen House in the north of England. We were immediately joined by Reverend Richard Seed and the initial team was born.

The name

We needed a name for the new hospice in order to start raising awareness and more importantly money. Helen was of course a child looked after by her parents supported by Sister Frances. We decided not to use the name of a child and did not want to just use a Saint's name as we wanted the hospice to be multi-faith in nature. We settled on the House Martin as name and early logo because of the way in which that bird returns to its same nesting site year on year after its long journey from Africa; respite from travel.

The concept

The concept was that the children's hospice would support families to look after their ill child in the manner that the family thought best. The family were the expert carers and we were there to learn from them and to provide professional support when and where it was needed. Many families had told us that if only they could have a break from the twenty four hour seven day a week responsibility from time to time they would be enabled to carry on the care of their child in their own home. They needed to be able to carry on nursing their child in the ways that they had developed and knew worked or to be able to show someone else exactly how to do it. They also told us of the importance of including the well siblings in any plan that would involve them being away from home and of including the well children in any treats planned for the children during their stay.

We would therefore provide a home from home atmosphere into which the whole family could come for short periods during the child's illness coupled with expert nursing and medical care when needed. In addition we would provide open access to the hospice at the time of the child's terminal illness if this was what the family required.

Raising awareness

The awareness raising exercise took two distinct lines. The public quickly grasped what we were trying to do. We were invited to all manner of groups to talk and explain our idea and money raising initiatives began to spring up all over Yorkshire and eventually the north of England. The professional bodies were a lot more difficult to convince, with most paediatricians wedded to the ideas that these were very rare cases and were best looked after in hospital or at home and a hospice facility had little to offer. Many lectures were given to postgraduate groups all over the country explaining, as Sister Frances had explained to us. Gradually professional support started to grow.

The Site

Next we needed a site on which to develop the hospice. In order to provide the atmosphere that we had in mind we needed it to be easily accessed by road and if possible by rail, to be near or in a town and its facilities and not to be on the site of a hospital or existing adult hospice. Estate agents provided details of several large houses and we visited some disused hospital buildings and many other potential existing buildings. All had merit but all had problems and we finally concluded that we would only be able to realise our vision by building from new. Richard heard that within his parish of Boston Spa a field might be available to buy but we would need planning permission to build. It was close to motorways, close to a small town with a friendly and supportive general practice, ideal for our purpose. After a number of minor and a few major traumas the field was bought and planning permission obtained.

The team grows

Two key individuals now joined us; first, the architect Michael Wildblood. Michael immediately grasped the idea of a place of refuge or respite and developed the idea into that of a harbour around which he based his initial designs for the building. Next came Lenore Hill our head nurse. Lenore again took our early ideas and developed them into a working plan. She and Michael then refined and developed the building and started to equip it ready to receive the first families. We benefited greatly at this time by visiting Helen House. Here the staff shared with us the way in which they worked and showed us those parts of their building which worked well and those that they would wish in the light of experience to redesign. Michael and Lenore were able therefore to incorporate this experience into our design for the new building and our methods of working.

The care team were recruited by Lenore and we started their training. It was important that the team members brought their individual professional skills but also that they understood and contributed to our philosophy. Thus the building and this training combined together and enabled the initial dream to be realised.

sharing our experience

We have since been able to welcome those in the planning stages of new hospices throughout the UK and abroad and provide them with our model of practice which has now had the benefit of twenty-one years of experience and development. It is crucial to the development of the children's hospice movement that continuing development based on research continues to take place and Martin House is seeking to place itself at the forefront of this work.

Full circle: Hazel Brown

Being born and bred in Boston Spa I remember playing as a child in the field where Martin House now stands. When building work started my Dad, along with other local residents, watched as the strange pointed building rose into view and wondered what on earth was being built. I never could have imagined that now aged fifty-six I would still be playing football and having water fights on that same field, but with not quite so much energy now.

I'd reached a time in my life when I thought I might like to work with children and young people, so I picked up the phone and rang to see if I could come and visit Martin House and have a chat. All went well and the day came for my interview. This was the day when Martin House staff were remembering the tragic loss of life in the Twin Towers; I thought then that this might just be a very special place. Six and a half years on no two days are quite the same. I've met some amazing people, families and colleagues, and I've done things that I would never believe I could with the help and support of a great team.

The opening of Whitby Lodge has made a huge difference to our young people and it has been great to see personalities evolve as teenage independence kicks in. Twenty one years must have seen some changes, but the welcome cup of tea and a piece of cake has always been the same and I'm sure it will continue.

© Bindy Pease

From Small beginnings

The hard work begins

I had been quite involved at an early stage with Frances Dominica, Helen and Helen House. In 1980 when we moved as a family away from Oxford to Boston Spa on my appointment as the new Vicar, I expected my involvement with the Hospice was finished. How wrong I was to be. In 1982 some of the Leeds paediatricians approached me to ask whether I would be willing to consider being involved in trying to provide a Northern Hospice for children. In agreeing, however, it soon became obvious that they were hoping, trusting and even expecting that I would actually co-ordinate the team and be the catalyst; so our hopes, hard work, difficulties, joys and sorrow began.

The Appeal office was a window sill in the back room of a High Street shop. We had no site, no money, we did no feasibility study, and we really did "step out" in faith. There was a splendid formal launch of the Martin House Appeal in the Civic Hall in Leeds, after which time the Yorkshire Post sponsored the Appeal. Their launch was an amazing day, with Jimmy Saville quickly becoming involved. This was the occasion when the public became really involved and after many months of "behind the scenes" trustees meetings our plans were launched. It was and remains a great tribute to the people of Yorkshire who have always taken this Hospice for children to their hearts. They have supported it, encouraged our plans and never wavered in generosity – truly wonderful.

A small team gradually came together and we decided on the name Martin House. We agreed on this for two reasons. Firstly a lot of the inspiration of St Martin was important to us in what we hoped to achieve. Martin was a fourth Century soldier, who had been forced to adopt the profession of his faith. Confronted one day by a man begging he cut in half his cloak and gave one half to the other man, retaining the other half for himself. It was in this action that he felt in the eyes of the beggar he had seen Christ. Such an example of costly sharing, empathy and an unconditional standing alongside and with the needy, were we felt the essential qualities that should be the philosophy of Martin House. In that name St Martin was our inspiration and Martin House was to be and still is a place that accepts without conditions those families whose children have a life threatening illness. They know the feeling of desperation and loneliness, Martin House walks alongside them in deep companionship. The second reason for the name was the House Martin, which was the orginal logo. This symbolized the House Martin, resting under the eaves of houses and outbuildings, receiving shelter and warmth, before flying off with its young for the winter for summer sun elsewhere- and then returning again next year. This showed how Martin House would always be here to offer shelter and even sanctuary to those who needed it, at their greatest time of need.

So Martin House began, with much symbolism but with great simplicity. Indeed, we always felt that an uncomplicated structure, an open and welcoming approval would be the greatest asset in a House where the children and families would always come first.

The inestimable support of the sisters

The Sisters of the Order of the Holy Paraclete in Whitby agreed overwhelmingly at their summer chapter to be a spiritual, praying anchor and work where appropriate on the Care Team. Their decision was amazing. I had gone to speak to their Chapter about our project, but at the time had nothing really definite, just a hospice for children. Their support meant that for ten years they lived at Martin House and were in so many ways crucial to the overall success. They reconciled many people who had been opposed to the hospice being built on the field where it now is. They also partially resolved the situation with people who maybe felt that I had neglected the parish during the appeal for the Hospice. The Sisters in many ways were the core of the Hospice, in retrospect the ten years of their physical, praying presence were essential. Although no longer physically present, their prayers for us continue. We are deeply grateful to them.

Perseverance

Of course the Appeal was not without its huge problems. There were disputes as to where the Hospice should be built, endless disappointments, planning setbacks that resulted in an Appeal to the Secretary of State, a serious fraud court case and all the subsequent publicity. At every major hurdle the one issue that remained constant was the support and generosity of countless people that were determined that Martin House would succeed. There were a few occasions when I very nearly gave up, especially after all the work made me ill and I was rushed to hospital.

Laying the Foundation Stone

The greatest moment of all was in November 1986 when HRH the Duchess of Kent came to lay the foundation stone assisted by the brothers and sister of Zoe, David and Scott, who had virtually become our first "Founding Families." How wonderful they were, as they were interviewed by the media and talked so openly about the pressure on families when a loved child is diagnosed with a life threatening illness. That day the Duchess touched the hearts of so many families, groups, trustees and local people. We knew Martin House had arrived at last. The Duchess returned as Patron to open the Hospice a year later and this time was met by the head nurse, Lenore Hill, another inspired appointment. We owe a huge debt to Lenore, who not only spent much time learning with our "Founding Families", but who also made contact with many other families who would use Martin House. She became deeply respected by professionals and families alike and like the Sisters laid down strong foundations.

Therefore Martin House, despite many up-hill struggles, arrived on this beautiful, open site. The Archbishop of York, Dr John Habgood, when he dedicated the Chapel and Hospice building said that when a project like this had struggled, and there was "blood in its very foundations", it would indeed be a blessing to many. We knew because we had struggled so hard for Martin House to become a reality that it would succeed. It is only when something has been so difficult that it is appreciated and valued when finally achieved.

coming of age

I remain deeply grateful for all those who have remained faithful to the vision of Martin House and what has been achieved over the years. Thank you to Friends groups and those who have donated generously over the years, Sisters, staff and above all the children and families who make Martin House the unique, wonderful, inspiring place it has truly become.

Therefore Martin House came to birth twenty-one years ago. Since then there has been laughter and sorrow, moments of great soul searching and question, but above all a House that in empathy stands deeply with those families during their greatest need in life. We have been fortunate to have staff and volunteers who are all committed to the care of the families who come and for whom we solely exist. It is truly a place of inspiring generosity; like St Martin centuries before when he shared spontaneously and deeply with another person and in that action made himself vulnerable. Twenty-one years seems a long time and Martin House has "come of age" – but it will forever stay young because it is here for all the young people who need its support and encouragement.

Derek Chapman

As Richard Seed has noted, the Sisters at Whitby played a large part in the formation of Martin House. When I took early retirement from being financial director of a large international company in 1987 I decided to take a retreat with the nuns. This was led by Sister Marianne Eva who had previously held senior medical posts. I remember discussing with her there my ambitions in retirement which included charitable work as yet undefined. Some months later I was surprised by the then Chairman of Martin House, Angus King, calling round to my house to invite me to become a trustee and review the finacial controls. An unusual example of the Sisters' early influence.

© Michael Wildblood

The Architect's tale

The Silent wish

I remember the talk and rumours in Wetherby in the summer of 1984 of the planned children's hospice to be built in Boston Spa and my silent wish to be involved as its architect. The opportunity came when Ford Longman telephoned in early November and asked to come to see me, to explain what a children's hospice sought to achieve and to invite Wildblood Macdonald to compete to be the architect. He came in the late afternoon of the 19th November and from that moment I knew that the role had to be ours.

On his suggestion I drove to Oxford a week later to visit Helen House, at the time the only children's hospice in the world, and its leader Sister Frances. I spent the day talking to staff and parents, playing with the children and washing up. I learnt more in those few hours than a term of lectures could ever achieve. Not wishing to lose what I had experienced, I pulled into the first lay-by I came to on the Banbury Road and spent over an hour capturing the magic of the day on a dictaphone before continuing on my journey home to Yorkshire.

My first impression of Helen House was one of love exuding from the entire household and of people caring for each other in a shell of bricks and mortar that was school, holiday camp, but chiefly home all rolled into one. That was what we had to bring to the construction of Martin House.

Over that Christmas, Peter Macdonald, other colleagues and I spent every hour available to us in preparing a concept, producing drawings and constructing a balsa wood model to demonstrate what we could do. (The model is still hanging on our meeting room wall). I made the presentation to the then Reverend Richard Seed and his fellow Trustees on the 18th January 1985. I closed with a slide of my children Tom and Shan throwing snowballs at each other and the comment that my best qualification for being the Martin House architect was my being the father of two children. Tears and a lump in my throat made it very difficult to finish that sentence.

The good news for us came the following Monday and the design work started in earnest.

The hospice as a harbour

As the designs developed, the three buildings of the original concept were reduced to two, the Chapel becoming annexed to the Sisters' Home, but our intent for the buildings to provide protection and shelter was there from the start. The analogy of a harbour was in that first presentation, not only in my explanation of the shape of the buildings, but also in the grading of the grounds away from the hospice; from protected terrace to lawn to wild garden, to give the children a range of play depending upon their sense of adventure.

The design of the buildings is individual. Whilst wanting to relate to the vernacular of Boston Spa in the choice of materials (limestone walls and clay pantiled roofs), we needed Martin House to have an identity of its own; one that recognised children in its scale through low eave heights, low cill heights and other means.

Everyone was helpful in the procurement of the buildings. After the successful appeal against the refusal of outline planning permission, the Leeds City Council and everyone else in the building process worked co-operatively to achieve its successful completion and it opened its doors to the children and their families in August 1987. The design won the RIBA Yorkshire Regional Award in 1988.

Ongoing involvement

My colleagues and I have been extremely privileged, not only to help Martin House with its original construction, but also with the designs for various alterations and additions that have occurred since that time. The Seminar Room was completed in 1993, but the major change came with the conversion of the Sisters' Home to form a 'Teenage Unit' and the construction of a new chapel, which were completed in 2002. This was the fulfillment of a dream for Lenore Hill and something she had talked about ever since her appointment as Head of Care in 1986.

The new chapel is a very special design for me. The passing through the thick drystone clad wall to a light and airy chapel might be to some the getting away from the busy activity of the hospice to a space of peace and quiet, but to others it is intended to represent the passing through death to something wonderful beyond. I believe that it has been successful in overcoming the resistance to the loss of the original chapel and its conversion to a 'den' for the 'teenagers'!

The latest project, completed earlier this year, was literally to bring the fundraisers and other helpers under the same roof.

Peter Macdonald, my current business partners Philip Wright and Stuart Fullerton, job architects Catherine Hewitt and Mike Burkett, Tommy Scholefield, all my other colleagues and I should like to thank Martin House for our involvement in their amazing work over the years. We send our congratulations for its 21st Birthday and wish it every success for the next 21 years and many years beyond.

34

Realising the Dream

Growing the vision

I felt thrilled, excited, daunted and honoured to be appointed the first Head of Care (then called Head Nurse) by the Trustees of Martin House. I was impressed by the compassion of those who had brought this dream so far. I was also impressed when I met the architect, Michael Wildblood, and realised how his commitment and vision would be so instrumental in creating a place worthy of the families it was to serve.

Of course, if I had realised then how the reality of the vision we had would grow like Topsy I may well have been too frightened to take the job. Fortunately it grew slowly and I had time to grow with it.

I was greatly helped and encouraged in the beginning by Edith Anthem, the Head Nurse at Helen House, who was to become a good friend and colleague over the years. I was impressed by her story of how involved Helen's parents had been in the vision and reality of Helen House, and I realised, as did she, that its success was based on their intimate knowledge of the needs of families in their position.

Families at the centre

The needs of the children and their families had to be central to all that we did at Martin House. I was helped enormously by those families who had been alongside the trustees from the beginning of the appeal. They were amazingly generous in giving their time and sharing their knowledge and their hopes of what Martin House would become for them. They shared so much of their broken dreams, their daily struggles; the disappointments they had experienced in services which they felt had failed them. Their honesty and vulnerability were amazing and helped us to avoid some of the mistakes which I am sure we would have made without their input. They spent hours checking the nursing history sheets and other necessary paperwork, to make sure that we asked the questions they thought were important in order to care for the children in the way they wanted us to.

Being allowed to spend so much time in the families' homes, hearing their stories and understanding their frustrations and the things they valued in services they used was such a gift to me – and I'm sure of inestimable value in starting us off on the right track.

Invaluable Support

We had several huge advantages right from the start at Martin House. Our trustees, the ones who had first had this vision, were really committed to it. It mattered to them that it worked for the children and families. They trusted those of us who were appointed by them to realise the dream. They were interested, supportive, and available always, but did not interfere in the day to day work of the hospice.

The other huge support which we had was from the other professionals involved with the children. Right from the beginning we had generous input of time from the specialist paediatric services in teaching and training our staff. We knew that if we were to help the children with complex needs who would want to use our service we would need their support and expertise. Throughout the last 21 years the therapists, nurses, doctors and others working in the NHS and with the specialist disease and other charities have been generous teachers in our staff training programmes. Whenever we have needed advice or support in the care of particular children it has always been freely given.

Sharing expertise

In our turn we have been pleased when other professionals have recognised our increasing expertise with children who often have rare conditions and very difficult symptom control issues and have turned to us for help. We have had many really great doctors working with us over the years, GPs, adult palliative care physicians and more recently paediatricians. All have brought knowledge and gifts which have benefited the children. I feel special mention must be made of Dr. Mick Brady, who has been with us from the beginning and at one period, during a sabbatical from his practice, worked with us full time. His knowledge and expertise is amazing, but it is his ability to be alongside families which is also such a gift. I would like to quote the words of a beautiful 18 year old girl who was with us for terminal care and who said of Mick, "He stands head and shoulders above any other doctor I have met. From the moment he introduced himself to me he has treated me with respect, he has never patronised me, he has made sure that I understand everything, and he has left me in control."

Listening to the families

Control is something which we always felt strongly should remain with the families themselves. Each family has their own way of caring for their child, and our task was to adapt our ways to accommodate their methods and wishes. This is their child, their experience, and our place was to be enablers, not to take over or impose our views. Listening was always very important to us; listening to their stories, but also to what they wanted from us, what they needed us to be for them or to do for them. One size definitely does not fit all.

Of course, listening to a family and carrying out care in the way that they want it to be done sounds much simpler than it is! Families are made up of individuals. The sick child, the Mum, the Dad and the brothers and sisters may all have different views about where would be best to be as death approaches, whether or not to tube feed, whether some new symptom control drug should be tried, whether to try some new experimental treatment as part of a drug trial. There are no right or wrong answers really other than what is right or wrong for this family. We learnt that listening to parents, or whole families together, could be valuable in enabling them to hear each other. As we, and they, heard the different fears and anxieties expressed sometimes a consensus could be reached. This was not always true, of course, and some families find it very hard to be open with each other (or even with themselves?) about their fears and anxieties and it makes it much more complex and more challenging for those of us around to get things as right as possible for them.

The children

Children who are sick are still children first. They have the same range of needs and wishes to live a fulfilled and satisfying life. These children may be going to have a shorter life, but we want to help them live as rich a life as possible. Many of our children become progressively more disabled by their illnesses; their cares become more complex, more draining, and more full time for their families. All of this has huge financial as well as emotional, physical, spiritual and mental consequences for the whole family.

The moment of diagnosis (which often follows a long and frustrating journey in itself) may be the beginning of bereavement, and the first experience of the many 'little deaths' that the parents live with throughout their child's life. Siblings, often much loved and valued, can feel sidelined by the needs of their sick brother or sister, or can take on parental type responsibilities as they learn to tube feed and carry out other cares – particularly where more than one of their siblings is sick or disabled. This can sound like a lot of loss from the outside. Many families also talk of the richness their sick child brought to their lives, the turning upside down of their previous values and of what was important to them. The gift of a smile, of beautiful eyes, of hurdles overcome, of the child's achievements, however small others may percieve them to be, are now prized and treasured.

All these complexities in the lives of the children and families, and our desire to help parents attain the richest possible life for their sick and well children, for themselves and their extended families, led to a lot of the decisions and service provision made at Martin House.

selecting the team

The first of these decisions, made at the very beginning, was the mix of team and the way that the team would work. We always sought to have a rich mixture of skills and personalities. We had more nurses than any other group, but from a mix of appropriate nursing backgrounds. We have also had physiotherapists, occupational therapists, teachers, a youth worker, nursery nurses, psychologists, social workers, music and art therapists and others. Everyone worked together, working shifts, caring for the children and families and helping with the care of the house. All were asked to be willing to share their skills and to enable one another in order to give the best possible care throughout the twenty four hours in the House or in the children's own homes.

The appointment I felt most anxious about from the beginning was the 'cook.' I had in mind a middle aged motherly lady who would welcome children and parents into her kitchen. Someone who would help the children to bake and create the real home from home atmosphere we were looking for. The kitchen was quite central in the design of the house and is often, in many homes, the place where everyone congregates. I was very fortunate in the two people who helped me to interview for the team. One was a local clinical psychologist and the other the nurse manager I had worked for in the hospital. I had told them that I hoped God would drop the right person in my lap, as I felt that this appointment was so crucial to the atmosphere we wanted to create. Well, as all who know us are aware, God did not drop a middle aged, motherly lady, but a young man, a chef called Robin. What a star he has been in creating, with the help of his wonderful volunteers, just that atmosphere we were looking for.

We were also very fortunate in our early years to have the involvement on our care team of sisters from the Order of the Holy Paraclete in Whitby. I have always felt that if we want to care for people in any meaningful way, then we must care for the spirit of that person as well as their body. The sisters, with the chaplains, were very generous in their understanding of spiritual as being much wider than religious care. What feeds the spirit of this child?... football? ... art? ...music?... nature? Religious support was available to anyone who wanted it, with regular services in the chapel, and other ministries available as and when the families wished to use them. The sisters and chaplains were also very aware of the needs of families of faiths other than Christian, and enabled the rest of the team to honour the traditions and festivals of Muslim, Jewish, Hindu and Buddhist families.

The arrival of the first families

One of the biggest joys for me was when we took our first children and families into the House. All the preparation and choosing of equipment, furnishings and bedding and suddenly it all came to life and began (hallelujah) to be untidy! I was convinced that I had forgotten to order something vital (like beds?) but nothing obvious came to light. Parents who had helped with the appeal and all the preparations were now staying in Martin House. One wonderful Mum (now a trustee) had believed she might never use it, but was there with her family. Families were very reassuring when asked if it met their expectations. They said that it was even better than they had hoped. The best moment for me, though, was when the mothers all ended up in the Jacuzzi one

© paulcarter-photography.co.uk

evening with a bottle of wine – laughing and talking and sitting rubber ducks on their heads. One told me she could not remember the last time she had just laughed and laughed like that. Another said that she realised that she still existed as a person and was not just her daughter's mother. (A lot of parents over the years have valued our use of their names, saying that they are often introduced as John's mother or Katy's father).

I feel that one of the most important things Martin House can do is to recharge the parent's batteries; to spoil them a bit and give them an experience of being cared for and valued themselves. Another important job is to give value to the brothers and sisters, to see them as precious in their own right. Obviously our care of the sick children is central to the family recharging. If they didn't trust us they could never relax. There is often such a sense of community among the families when they stay together in the house. I really feel that whole families staying enhance the atmosphere and enable such a lot of sharing. Parents have often told us that it was the only place they felt that they could really be themselves; to laugh or cry, to express their anger or their joy.

maintaining contact

Each member of the team became a contact person for a group of families and would try to make sure that they were receiving whatever they needed from us. Initially they also followed up the families who had been bereaved with phone calls and visits. However, it soon became apparent that the work load became too great for the same people to continue to work with new families, and also support the families whose children had died. Tessa from Helen House kindly came and talked to the team about how they organised their support for bereaved families and helped us to decide what would be appropriate for us.

Going forward

Other people are going to explain how so many aspects of our work have developed over the years. We now have parents groups and groups for well siblings, as well as our longer established bereaved children's groups, and grandparents groups. We have the teenage and young adult house – named Whitby Lodge by one of the teenagers to remember the sisters from Whitby who had lived in it originally. Our community work has grown and is more formalised. I feel that it is important to say that all of these initiatives have come about directly because of the feedback we have had from families about the services they would like us to provide for them. Martin House is still listening and responding.

As we have grown, and the number of families we support has also grown so dramatically from the few we knew when we first opened, we have had the same pressures as all health care providers face in trying to meet needs within the available resources. The generous support of the people of Yorkshire and beyond has enabled us to do far more than we ever dreamed possible, but of course we always feel inadequate when we look at the huge impact that these children's illnesses have on them and their families.

It is left to others, also, to write about the work of the administration and fundraising teams, but I would like to say how much I have always valued their real interest in the children and families whom they, as well as the care team, serve, and acknowledge that without their hard work none of this could happen. They work closely with us, and know some of the families, and do get some feedback about the value of the work of Martin House which is, of course, their work also. However, we also owe a huge debt of gratitude to the thousands of people who do not have the joy of knowing the incredible people who use Martin House – do not see the smiles of the children in the Jacuzzi or using special play equipment that their money has provided, and yet are so generous in giving their time and their money to enable the work to continue and to develop.

We have made many mistakes, and I am sure have not always met what families wanted from us. Some of the most painful mistakes for me have been when we have appointed people who have many gifts and qualities, but were not in the right place in Martin House. I have been amazed at the generosity of so many of our families who in the midst of all their own pain, of which anger is inevitably a part, have invariably been very forgiving of our mistakes and blunders. They can never appreciate the richness they have given to the lives of those of us who have been privileged to share a little bit of their life and their children with them.

Early memories and pictures

Twenty one years on the memories of the preparation, the cleaning and the excitement of the first families arriving remain strong. Members of the early team recall these times. The last story in this section is written three years after the opening of Martin House and shows how things were developing and working out for the families and for the team.

© paulcarter-photography.co.uk

I remember: Hazel Clough

Sitting nervously in the office above the shoe shop, looking around at the rest of the team and being amazed that Robin, who was sitting opposite me, managed to very calmly organise lunch each day for us all. When I think of the wonders he has performed here ever since I need not have been so impressed by the sandwich lunches!

The time before the families came, learning about each other, cleaning the house, preparing for the open days, showing around hundreds of people on the open days, and having some wonderfully inspiring talks on our study weeks. I particularly remembered Ede Anthem who was the head nurse at Helen House, for her encouragement and reassurrance.

In the midst of all the hectic preparations someone suggested that Lenore ought to make the first child's bed, she had been so careful with all the arragememts and had been looking forward to the day for so long when the first families would arrive. So we all stood around while Lenore made the bed and we applauded when she had finished. It was a very special moment

Then the privilege of working on that very first shift when the families arrived, we were all so nervous, we didn't want to overwhelm them, yet wanted them to feel welcome and in control. Our first families did so much to help us get started on the right track, they encouraged us and were willing to share their wishes with us, they helped us to learn how to truly be guided by the families.

Claire Hayes

At the start of Martin House the care team were all new; we started with a new building, some fantastic ideas and some very vulnerable families who were willing to take a chance. As a team member I was both excited and anxious (as well as a whole range of other feelings). We spent our time cleaning and tidying after the builders. This was a very valuable time for the new team, allowing us to talk whilst cleaning and organising, getting to know more about the people that we were working with. As families started to share their skills each day would bring new learning, new skills and new challenges. I was amazed at the families' generosity in sharing their precious children and knowledge, teaching us about their child's and their family's own individual needs. It was great being part of a team, if you did not know what to do or how to do it someone would show you and share their knowledge, or they would ask for your help and knowledge. Martin House is my other family.

© paulcarter-photography.co.uk

Andrea Topp

I heard about the fund raising campaign for Martin House when I was still a student nurse. I initially visited the site when it was only a muddy field and knew instinctively it was where I wanted to work. When all the building work was completed I applied for a position on the care team. I was beyond thrilled when I was successful. We even decided to delay our honeymoon as we were getting married only 48 hours before the new team were all starting and I didn't want to miss it.

I vividly remember our first morning all crammed together in an office in Boston Spa with Robin taking the sandwich order. I still had stars in my eyes from my recent wedding (Hazel and I still joke about that today). We had a trip to look round Martin House for the first time and then followed a hectic couple of weeks dodging the builders whilst we cleaned, hung curtains, unpacked furniture and equipment and very importantly bonded as a team. It was a special time and we were all full of high goals and aspirations and anxious to do our best for the families. We had a few study days together and then two weeks of showing people around who had fund raised for Martin House.

On the 14th August 1987 we were welcoming the first families to come and stay. I was lucky enough to be working that day. My first task was to take a vehicle to Leeds railway station to meet a mother and her daughter who were coming to stay. I was incredibly nervous, would I know what to say or would I let Martin House down at the first hurdle? I needn't have worried, everything fell in to place. They were tired from the journey and relieved to see a friendly face, and somehow I seemed to know what to say.

Those early days were a memorable time as we felt our way through what worked for the families. I think we all knew we were part of something unique and that has bonded us to this day. We had many fun times with the children but also some sad times. The death of the first child was hard for us all but we supported each other. There was a feeling that that was the reason we were there, to share the sad as well as the happy times with the families and to support and guide them in their choices. Martin House was quieter in those days and we worried as to whether enough families would want to come and stay. That seems laughable today when we are so busy and have expanded so much. I guess the foundations we laid in those early days produced a good working model for the future of Martin House.

It is hard to believe that is all 21 years ago. A lot of life has happened to us since then and we are all a bit older and wiser, but a few of that original team still remain. Many of us have performed a variety of roles within Martin House in that time . As well as working on the care team I myself have spent six years working in the community and five years on the team supporting the bereaved families. For all of those 21 years people have asked me the same question, 'How can you work there, isn't it too sad?' 21 years later the answer remains the same , 'Because Martin House makes a difference to the children and their families.' Through all these years I have never lost sight of the privilege of being a part of that.

Bernadette Murray

It felt like going into the unknown. I took a job with no building even to look round to see where I was going to work. I'd first heard about Martin House when I came to work at York District with Lenore. I'd heard about Helen House and Lenore's stories from her having spent time there with the team. I'd heard about her hopes of working on the team at Martin House. When she was appointed as Head of Care I was aware of her vision for its future and her concern to appoint the right team and to get the building right.

Lenore left York a year before Martin House opened. This meant that she had time to meet the families and find out what they wanted in terms of facilities and equipment. She had to do all the planning for the rooms and appoint a team to work there. She also was offering support to the families already referred or involved. This was a massive job for only one person on the care team side.

I'd never heard of Boston Spa until hearing about Martin House. My husband Tommy and I drove out one evening to find the village. I remember being struck by what a pretty place it was with all the soft-coloured stone work and lovely Georgian houses. We drove down to find the site; it was a large muddy field and the foundations were just being laid. Later I applied for a job and after being appointed we started work. As the building was not ready we met in the village above the fundraising office. We were all very nervous but excited to be there at the start. We were aware of the great trust placed in us by Lenore and the Trustees.

We had a month getting ready to open. This meant we had training days and also time to get to know each other. We were also visiting families at home. During this time Lenore asked me to visit a family in Manchester, as I knew the area. They had been travelling to Helen House for respite and now Martin House would be much nearer. Their son was very ill and they hoped to stay as soon as we opened. I was feeling apprehensive as this was my first home visit. When I arrived outside the house the curtains were drawn and I realized Chris had died. I went in tentatively to meet the family who were obviously distressed. They invited me to stay and listen to their story and wait with them until the undertaker arrived. I then went with one of the team to his funeral. His mum and brother came later to stay at Martin House as it was already planned they were going to stay. It was our first experience as a team of being alongside a bereaved family. I remember how we would sometimes be with his brother Stuart on the patio outside the bedroom as he screamed up at the stars for his brother. I then stayed in touch as their bereavement support person as the bereavement team was not set up at this stage.

Denise Quinn

Twenty-one years ago (with some trepidation) I handed in my notice to terminate my employment as a Staff Nurse at York Hospital to take up a post at a new children's hospice that had been built at Boston Spa. I was apprehensive; it was a new venture, only the second children's hospice in the world. Apart from the recent success of Helen House an untried and unproven addition to the care spectrum, a huge leap of faith. I felt I knew a lot about it though as in one of my previous jobs, on the Oncology Unit at St James Hospital, Leeds, our consultant Cliff Bailey had been proudly showing the plans and sharing his vision for the future of the hospice with anyone who stood still long enough to listen.

Lenore, who had been my ward sister in York, reinforced this along with a few ideas of her own; such as we wouldn't be serving chips more than once a week at mealtimes. In fact before we left the ward, Bernadette and I organised a survey of the opinions of parents and children to prove to her oven chips were not as nice as the real thing (even if they were supposedly healthier).

In July 1987 twenty-five very excited staff arrived to begin our first day and to initiate the many friendships, many of which still endure today. That first day consisted of meeting the office staff and some of the fundraisers and volunteers who had done such a fantastic job getting us to this point, and an awful lot of cleaning. The builders were behind schedule and hadn't handed over the building, everything was covered in a thick layer of dust, not all the flooring was in place, and lorries filled with furniture and equipment were pulling in at frequent intervals, needing to be unloaded. It was like Christmas wanting to know what was inside all the packing cases and underneath all the wrapping. I remember it as a very exhausting yet exciting day. At five o'clock Lenore and Robin Wood gathered us together on the stairs at the far end of the house near the multi-sensory room (then a garage) to thank us for our hard work and share their plans for the coming days. I remember looking down at the base of the spindles on the banister and noticing it was still covered in about an inch of dust that we'd missed, but not having the energy to do anything about it.

But the building took shape, everything found a home, and it was with pride that we welcomed our first children, David, Zoe and John for their first stay.

Over the intervening years we have seen many developments and changes to our care practices. At the time of opening none of the thirty-three children receiving care from the hospice had a gastrostomy tube, none were ventilated and all the boys diagnosed with Duchenne Muscular Dystrophy seemed to drive the high backed red Vessa chairs. For some children the only other respite care offered was on a hospital ward or in an old people's home. Our families travelled to Yorkshire for care from as far afield as the north of Scotland, Essex and Wales. With the expansion of the children's hospice movement our catchment area has thankfully reduced somewhat.

Because of the relatively small numbers of staff and families involved, everyone on the team multi-tasked. The community and bereavement teams were yet to evolve, and the various sibling and parent groups not thought of. What has not changed during our twenty one years is our philosophy that the needs and wishes of the families remain central to our service provision. Over the years families have had to deal with the increasing medicalisation of their homes. We live in a world of gastrostomies, tracheostomies, non-invasive overnight ventilation, spinal rods, complex care packages, (or lack of them), hickman lines and portacaths. All of this is now commonplace, each bringing the challenge of more complex symptom control, as children survive further into the disease process. However, the fundamental needs of the families and those caring for our special children remain largely unchanged.

No doubt over the next twenty-one years new challenges will continue to emerge. Our buildings have been adapted and enlarged, Whitby Lodge has come into being. Technology has changed, new treatments have been and will be devised, and members of a now much enlarged team will come and go. Unfortunately the need for the service we offer will remain.

© paulcarter-photography. co.uk

Pam Lineham

I loved my work on the post-natal ward and Special Care Baby Unit at Leeds General Infirmary, but after six years I was becoming increasingly frustrated at the shortage of staff and I felt unable to give proper care to the new mums and babies. My neighbour and friend suggested Martin House. "Martin House," I said, "never heard of it!"

Then having found out anything and everything possible about this wonderful new Children's Hospice only fourteen miles from where I lived, I went to see Lenore for an informal visit and chat. A year later I was interviewed and wonder of wonders got the job as a member of the care team. That was twenty one years ago and I'm still here.

How I felt on the first day

To be honest, there are many words to describe my first day at Martin House. We met upstairs in the fundraising shop in Boston Spa. The atmosphere was electric. I can remember feeling so nervous, excited, bewildered, consumed by many different emotions. We spent the day cleaning up after the builders, having first looked around this magnificent structure. I chatted all day to different members of the team (something I don't find particularly difficult!). It was fascinating finding out their different backgrounds. There were only twenty eight of us to start with. I sought out two fellow nursery nurses and we became niggle, naggle and noggle, don't ask me why. Although I had so many different feelings throughout the day when at the end of the day we all sat down exhausted, sweaty and dirty on the back stairs to give ourselves a well earned pat on the back, I couldn't have felt more proud and determined than ever before. I was on the care team of the second children's hospice in England – WOW!

I had definitely made the right decision to come and work here. Although over the years there have been many sad and harrowing shifts, overall it is the most rewarding place I could ever wish to work.

Jude Lyon

I first came to work at Martin House as a bank nurse in October 1990, eighteen years ago. I was very impressed at my interview with the facilities of Martin House and the philosophy of care that they embraced so when I was appointed I couldn't wait to start. Coming from a hospital setting this seemed the ideal place to care for families with a child with a life-limiting condition.

After I had been working on the bank at Martin House for eighteen months covering sickness, meetings and busy times, Lenore, our Head Nurse at the time, was struggling to get suitable staff for the care-team. One day as Lenore spoke of this I enthusiastically suggested that she had very good bank staff who would love to work more regularly but not full time.....including me! At this time the policy was that all staff on the care-team worked full time, and so this was going to be a real change. Lenore said she would give it some thought. After a while she decided to give two bank staff the chance of working three days a week on the team for a trial period of six months.

At our next bank staff meeting this was put to all the bank staff and there was great excitement about it. We had to apply in writing and I was nervous as I so wanted to work more often at Martin House. After people had gone home and looked at the possibility of fitting it in with family life only Joanne and I applied (phew!). We duly started the trial period on March 1st 1992. We were both very excited and determined to show it could work for the families as well as the team with part time hours.

As part of our role on the care team we were to be allocated a number of families for whom we would take responsibility; from their initial look around to keeping regular contact, checking how they are, making sure they have a booking and offering any further support necessary. Joanne and I were to be contact partners and our first referral came in the first week of us taking our places on the team.

My first contact family

I made the initial call to the family to arrange a visit to look around Martin House. I wrote a list of things I might say on the telephone to ease my nerves and made the call, realising that the family would probably feel nervous about it too. It is a big step for families to think about accepting respite support when up to this time they have provided all their child's cares within the family, often with no other help. I spoke to Jill Carr, Jeffrey's mum and introduced myself and the role Joanne and I would play in arranging their initial visit and then any future contact if they decided to accept the support Martin House had to offer. Jill was delighted to be coming for an initial look around. They were naturally apprehensive but also open minded about what it would be like. A date was agreed to suit them all and as I was on late duty that day I was able to conduct the tour. Joanne was on an early shift so this was ideal as she could meet the family too.

On March 15th 1992 the doorbell rang and I approached the door with my nerves rising again. Would I remember to tell them everything? Would they like it? Would I be able to answer all their questions? The first port of call was the dining room table for refreshment and some of our chef, Robin's, cakes. How could I fail in my quest to impress! Joanne was there to meet them and support me with the initial time getting to know each other. After the tea and cakes, a time which Jeffrey found difficult as he wanted to get straight into looking around, I took them to look in the lounge, library, music room and playroom. Jeffrey was so inquisitive and wanted to see every nook and cranny of the building, bedrooms, bathrooms and beyond into the garden. We barely touched on one place and he was off to enquire about the next.

Jeffrey, Jill and Tony all made my job very easy and it was a delightful afternoon. I was so proud of the facilities we had to offer and could see Jill and Tony visibly relax as we progressed through Martin House and out into the gardens. It took a little time as again Jeffrey wanted to see all around the gardens. I tried to reassure him that he could investigate further on his first visit, should they choose to come, but this was not soon enough! After investigating the tiger bridge, wheelchair swings and pathways we made our way back to the house. I offered another drink and chatted away with this lovely family. Jeffrey's sister, Alison, was away at university so unable to come for a look on this occasion but I was reassured that Jeffrey would be able to give her a very good account of our facilities!

I felt ten feet tall as they all left, thanking me for the tour and asking for their first booking to stay with us. I spoke to the Deputy Head of Care, asking how I had done? With a smile she gently said that we don't usually spend three and a half hours showing a new family around! Due to the flexibility of the team, my other duties that afternoon had been quietly dealt with to enable the visit to run smoothly despite the time taken! I have shown many families round since Jeffrey and his parents came and I still take great delight in introducing them to Martin House. My time management has improved since those early days too!

You will have gathered that the six month trial worked out well and since then other care team members have been able to balance home and work in this way. Joanne and I still continue our work on the care team and we are both very grateful to Lenore for giving us this opportunity.

Tony, Jill, Alison and Jeffrey Carr

Martin House first came to our attention years before it was built, when some friends had a sticker on their car for Martin House. We asked them what it was, and they explained that they were raising funds to build a children's hospice at Boston Spa. They were farmers who were felling trees and selling the wood to raise money. Little did we know that their enthusiasm for an unknown project 50 miles away would eventually play such an important part in our lives.

Some eight years later we were at a low ebb and like many families we were forced to accept our need for the care Martin House provided. When you have a child like Jeffrey with muscular dystrophy, it takes time to accept that caring 24 hours a day, day after day, takes its toll on the whole family, and that sharing the care with others is not an admission of failure. In the spring of 1992 we accepted a referral to Martin House. Soon after we were ringing the doorbell to make our initial visit with nervous anticipation. Since the moment we crossed the threshold Martin House and Boston Spa have become increasingly part of our family life.

Having been privileged to be part of that special family, Martin House, we have a wonderful store of memories, mostly happy, some hilarious and naturally some sad. We have seen changs in the building and the staff but one thing never changes, the love that envelopes you as you enter, and remains with you whether you are within the building or at the end of the phone at home at 3am.

At first it is difficult to let go and let someone else do the caring, but gradually the confidence grows, the work load can be shared, and eventually taken over by the care team. With that confidence Jeffrey enjoys hearing the latest gossip whilst making collages, listening to music or even supervising pancake making in the kitchen. Future developments and building work are always discussed in detail, from carpets to kitchen fittings, his interest is unbounded.

We have now come to realise that Martin House is the only place we can have a true holiday. We can go away from home to stay, enjoyable and precious as it may be, we just transfer the care to a different bedroom, a different bathroom and a different view. Martin House is a home for us but without the physical demands, offering a rare opportunity to do the things most people take for granted and allowing us to spend quality time with Jeffrey without the pressures of everyday life. Sundays are always a very special day for us at Martin House. Having to wake Jeffrey up, establish a breathing pattern having been ventilated all night, put on a spinal brace and leg splints, get dressed and then get him comfortable in his wheelchair takes time,

so getting to church at home for nine in the morning is extremely difficult. With so many willing hands getting to St Mary's at Boston Spa happens now like a well oiled machine(well nearly!). To return, having had a convivial coffee and a gentle stroll, to find lunch prepared by Robin is a luxury that we only find at Martin House.

The team who are Martin House are indeed a rare breed of people. Martin House is not just a building, it is a dedicated group of people whether part of the care team, kitchen staff, volunteers, office staff, administrators or fundraisers. They all give unreservedly of their time and talents to provide families with the love and support they need through often difficult and traumatic times. Martin House is not a place, it is a way of life for all of us, and it will remain in our hearts forever.

Section Two:
The Philosophy

© Bindy Pease

The philosophy guiding Martin House is woven into the very fabric of its being. At its core it is one of collaboration and respect between the families and the whole team who serve them in the hospice. This fundamental philosophy is described by Head of Care Sheila O'Leary and Trustee Jenny Wilkinson in Chapter Six. We see how it translates into practice from Jenny Wilkinson's experience both as a trustee and also from her personal experience as the mother of one of the first families to stay at Martin House.

The Philosophy

The guiding philosophy of Martin House derives from the conviction that the families we care for, and their choices, must be placed first in all our policies and care provision. We try to listen to, respect and value each member of the family, as individuals with their own needs.

The key to the fulfilment of our philosophy is flexibility; flexibility in management, in working arrangements and in attitudes to job content.

By this approach we hope to help the child and their family achieve a better quality of life, according to their wishes. We offer a well-informed choice of options as death approaches and seek to offer the best possible terminal care.

This is followed by support for the whole family in their bereavement with the ultimate aim of a new normality for them all, independent of our involvement, in which their child's life is always valued.

The guiding philosophy

The philosophy of hospice care

Hospice is described as a philosophy of care. Philosophy cannot be described easily, it refers to a certain kind of approach to a certain kind of, in this case, care. If we look at the word philosophy it comprises two words Philos which means love and Sophia which means wisdom. The hospice philosophy centres around the love and support offered to families and the wisdom that families bring about their children and their family.

Hospice is derived from the latin word Hospitium and means hospitality. Hospice care originated from the concept of offering a place of shelter and rest, or "hospitality" to weary or sick travellers on a long journey. The care did not focus purely on their clinical care but the holistic care required to ensure that the mind and body became rested and refreshed. In 1967 Dame Cicely Saunders first applied the term to the specialized care of people in the terminal phase of their illness. Since then the adult hospice movement has grown significantly.

Children's hospices

Helen House in Oxford opened in 1982. Martin House opened to families in 1987. The children's hospice philosophy was similar to that of adult hospices in the belief that care had to be holistic, but in other ways the model differed significantly. Children's hospices are available to any child and family in which there is a child with a life limiting condition. The hospice philosophy embraces an approach that encompasses physical, emotional and spiritual care. The interdisciplinary team enters into a relationship with the child and family in which a life journey is travelled; the route is often unpredictable with many mountains to climb. The family take the lead on their journey and the Martin House team are there to care and support the family in a way that best meets their individual needs.

Flexibility is vital

Martin house is committed to ensuring that families are able to make choices. We listen, respect and value each member of the family. The key to the fulfilment of our philosophy is flexibility. The philosophy affirms life and aims to achieve a better quality of life. Following the death of their child support is offered to the whole family with the ultimate aim of a new normality for them all, independent of our involvement, in which their child's life is always valued.

This philosophy is illustrated in practice in the personal account that follows. It is told by Jenny Wilkinson, mother and trustee, whose daughter Zoë was one of the very first children to use Martin House.

The philosophy of martin house in practice

'I have been involved with Martin House for all of its 21 years, and a few before then. It has always had that special quality, even before the building came into being. When our daughter was first diagnosed with a terminal illness I felt that I must be the only person who was bearing such a tragedy. The hospital help was adequate but there was still a feeling of isolation. I contacted one of the adult hospices near by and whilst they offered to help if I was really desperate they did not cater for the needs of a sick child. Of course family and friends were there but the responsibility of caring for your beloved daughter whilst watching her deteriorate over a predicted life expectancy of between six months to five years was enormous.

Having heard via my sister that Richard Seed and Cliff Bailey were trying to fund raise to build a children's hospice near Leeds I eagerly contacted Richard. From that moment I experienced the caring that was to become Martin House. Despite being busy with Parish duties and fundraising activities Richard kept in constant contact with us and was there when we needed. The little room in the back of the shoe shop in Boston Spa (the centre of the fundraising) became a refuge on many occasions. Already the "caring" associated with Martin House had started.

There was a considerable amount of fund-raising to be done and this involved television publicity. Although interviews were not always easy, the positive aspects helped us to find something useful that could come from such a devastating situation.

When Richard showed me the field where Martin House was to be built I had the most overwhelming feeling that this was indeed a special place. As we stood in the sunshine gazing at the field I could hear the long grass swishing and the trees gently rustling around the perimeter. It was one of those magical moments and I still frequently recall that image to mind. Watching the building grow gave me a positive focal point and with great pride my husband and I watched our sons help to lay the foundation stone with Sally and Stephen (sister and brother to two other sick children) and the Duchess of Kent. Eventually Lenore was appointed as Head Nurse and despite being involved with the massive "shopping list" to furnish the hospice she started to set the pattern for Martin House's philosophy. She visited all the families in their homes, phoned constantly and made herself available whenever she was needed.

Finally the day of the official opening arrived. The idea was that the first families should stay for the weekend but therein lay my problem! I truly believed in all that I had promoted about Martin House – the need for respite care – for sick children as well as their families; but even the idea of packing,

albeit just for a weekend, was exhausting. We were five years into Zoë's illness and I could not face having my routine altered. My sick daughter, my boys and my husband were my little world – that is how I coped and I didn't want it changing. However, the more I thought about it the more I knew that I must steel myself. I owed it to all the fundraisers, the future families who would use it and to myself, so I put my money where my mouth was and I went – telling Lenore that it would only be for ONE night. The warmth that enfolded me there was amazing. There were other families under exactly the same pressure, also trying to cope with watching their children slowly die and yet trying to maintain a normal family life for their healthy children. We derived great comfort and companionship from each other. We also laughed together as well as cried and there was always someone to give you, "the all important Martin House hug". One night spread into two and gradually I discovered walking into the village for a cream cake knowing that Zoë was in the very capable hands of the Care Team, being treasured and nurtured just as I would be doing. The late hours that the two of us kept were not a problem for the Team, neither was the fact that we then both surfaced in the morning after eleven. My Mum and sisters and close friends came to visit and the "home from home" ethos started. One day seemed to follow another very swiftly and gradually the end of the week arrived. Gentle murmurings started about when I thought I might like to leave – there were others waiting. I now hold the dubious reputation of being the person who reluctantly came for one night and had to be "thrown out". On a more serious note, had I needed to stay it would have been fine.

One of the most important benefits of that time was that I found myself again. Having been cosseted in the big, soft, cosy blanket of Martin House I went home refreshed and in the knowledge that Martin House was there and I only had to pick up the phone and support was waiting. We had to wait five years to make use of the hospice but families now can receive the support and respite care they need much earlier. As there were not so many families in the beginning we were able to stay at Martin House one week every month for the next four months until Zoë died there just before Christmas. Throughout all this difficult time the Team were there to comfort and support us. They were never intrusive – just there. Gradually we began to re-build our lives. We do have happy memories as well as sad ones of the little girl who was, and still is, part of our family and she is thought of and spoken about constantly - it's just that we can only see her in our minds and photos.

The Board of Trustees

We have always stayed in contact with Martin House, despite the inevitable changes in the Team, although there are still a few left from the beginning. It has always had a very special place in our hearts but I was so surprised and proud when I was quite recently asked to become a Trustee. I felt very privileged to be asked to join such a Board. Although the Heads of Care and Finance handle all the routine matters, the Trustees are ultimately responsible for controlling the management and administration of Martin House. The Trustees offer varied expertise ranging from Business/Industry/Charity, Financial, Legal and Medical experiences to bereaved parents. At meetings considerable thought is given to such items as the best investment of funds, whether new buildings or extensions are necessary, how to continue the progress of Martin House as a flagship; more recently, for example, investing in increasing the knowledge base of children's palliative care through research. The Trustees all work purposefully in the background using their specialist knowledge to solve any problems be it financial, legal or pastoral, as well as being prepared to stand with a collecting tin. We now attend training days especially devised for us so that we can learn even more about the different aspects related to the day-to-day work involved in the efficient running of Martin House.

One of my responsibilities at the moment is to complete an annual inspection of the hospice and send a report to the Health Care Commission. This is a legal requirement to ensure Martin House is providing a good service, but it also gives the Trustees a better insight into daily life in the hospice and confirms our belief in the management. Amongst other things I am required to talk with a cross section of members of the Team to ensure that they are happy with the way they are expected to work. Not all establishments have the notion that everyone, handyman, housekeeper, office staff, fundraisers and carers are the same – each has their own expertise. So far everyone has enthused about this system. I am also required to check with the families that they are happy with the service offered. I am privileged to be able to see some of the letters received from parents. Praise and gratitude abound. It gives me such a glow to know that families are still benefiting tremendously from Martin House and it is proof enough that Martin House is getting it right and keeping to its successful ethos.

Lenore was there from the beginning until 2004, and she set the foundations for the Martin House philosophy. With a change of leadership there could have been a complete difference, but Sheila has taken up the helm and continued steering successfully on. Of course there are new ideas, we are continually growing and evolving, but the ethos has never changed. It often surprises people to know that despite the nature of what the hospice is, it remains a happy place with sad moments.

Trusteeship is an enormous responsibility, but we all believe in the need for, and the importance of, Martin House. We are proud of the way it has developed and its continuing success. Caring for families in their homes has increased, there is far more bereavement care for adults and siblings and more research is now being carried out. What has never changed is Martin House's basic philosophy. Flexibility in all things is paramount.'

Families at the centre

This flexibility has ensured we do not offer a take it or leave it service, that families have a true choice. Throughout the 21 years the philosophy of listening, respecting and valuing the families who choose to use Martin house has helped to shape the service and environment we now offer. Over the years we have known families from many different backgrounds. Having a child with a life limiting condition does not exclude any member of society. We have realized that each family has their individual way of coping. Even though groups of children may have the same condition the journey can be very different. Medical and technological advances have meant that for some children their life expectancy has increased.

The diversity of the families is complemented by the diversity of the team. The families and children have taught us so much not only about the service we offer but how to cope and live life in the face of adversity on a journey they would never have chosen, but one they will complete weaving together the emotional physical and spiritual elements.

Trustees Roland Parker and Donald Swarbrick chatting over a relaxed lunch with Dr.Mike Miller

Section Three:
Stories from Martin House

People have all kinds of imaginings about what a children's hospice is like...a lot of them sad ones. This can make it difficult for parents to cross the threshold and bring their child to Martin House. If they decide to come does that mean they are giving up that all essential hope? However once families have experienced Martin House they say it is not like that at all. Rather they talk of it as a wonderfully easy place to be, relaxed and truly full of life. Perhaps the best way to appreciate this is through the following stories of day to day life, written by the children, families and care team.

A day in the life of martin House

No two days are ever alike at Martin House, but here I attempt to give a feel of what could be a typical day…

7.10am   The clunk of car doors heralds the arrival of the day shift and relief for their night shift colleagues. A few minutes later, with their first coffee of the day, they get handover and an inkling of how the day may pan out….."Trevor's deteriorated……Susie's feed pump is playing up….Akki's Mum needed to talk until the early hours…. the carrots and spuds are peeled….a pair of Superman boxers have gone walkabout….will someone ring Jimmy's about Tony's blood test…and can we ask the doctor to see the baby admitted yesterday." The night staff concludes her messages about the children and their families with, "and that, troops, is your little family."

7.30   The day staff make an outline plan of who will look after whom but with the common understanding that support is mutual; this is team-work.

8.00   Some children are beginning to stir. There are medicines to check, equipment to test, pads and nappies to change and baths to fill. Well siblings sharing a room with a poorly brother or sister emerge on the corridor and toddle up to the kitchen and the smell of hot buttered toast. Robin, the chef, has arrived and begins preparing a lunch time delight.

9.10   Two young lads with muscular dystrophy are battling out a Star Wars encounter on the play station in the Activities Room.

9.35   A cacophony of drums and cymbals throbs from two siblings in the Music Room under the supervision of the music therapist. Later she will play the flute and guitar to two children too poorly to leave their beds and encourage them to express themselves on chimes and bells.

10.10 In the Multi-Sensory Room a child is cradled by one of the team. Together they watch the projected soft coloured shades of skies drifting across the ceiling and walls to a background of Celtic music. There are no words from the child, nor ever will be, but today there is the reward of a rare smile witnessed by Mum and Dad who peep through the door.

11.05 Trevor's parents are led into the quiet sitting room with the doctor. Trevor is dying only two days from his eighth birthday. They emerge damp eyed hand in hand and return to their son's room to face the cruellest hours of any parent's life.

11.40 In the main sitting room a sing-song is in full swing with everyone and anyone. "The Grand Old Duke of York" follows on from "Octopus's Garden" and "Old MacDonald."

12.15pm "Lunch is ready everybody" calls Robin and the dining room area begins to fill. Wheelchairs, pushchairs, trolleys and knee-nursed babies, Mums, Dads and the team together round the laden table. Robin offers choices including a special lemon cheesecake made by a volunteer. This coming together is an important ritual of the day.

1.25 The late shift begin to arrive already sensing Trevor's Mum and Dad's absence from the table.

1.45 Susie's family are packed and ready to depart after their deserved respite stay, their car stuffed with all the paraphernalia of looking after a seriously ill child. The sadness of departure is eased by the knowledge of their next booking a few weeks hence.

2.30 The "lates" have joined the "earlies" in a two hour cross over. The two boys with muscular dystrophy want to go to the cinema.

3.10 Carol, a long standing volunteer arrives and before departing in less than two hours will have produced a feast of cakes for an army.

3.40 The "earlies" have just gone. A space station junk model is being constructed by a child in the Art Room whilst another little girl giggles at the sensational joy of finger painting with one of the artists.

4.52 Trevor dies peacefully and painlessly, held preciously in the arms of Mum and Dad. No one ever gets used to this. It is our ultimate purpose but we feel most useless. When the time is right the doctor and care team slip out of the room leaving Mum and Dad with their son. The sad news is quietly passed around the team; one is gluing the final antenna onto the intergalactic space craft, one is filling tea pots, two are checking drugs. The news is acknowledged with a knowing nod. The shift continues….it cannot stop.

5.20 Tea is understandably quieter but friendly. A plan of initial support is already being planned in Trevor's room. Grandparents are phoned and will arrive by 7pm.

6.10 The new family arrive with Adam, almost stumbling through the door in collapsing relief. A little later, but not just yet, they will be told about Trevor – a necessary telling to avoid embarrassment when families meet, but a reminder too of what they may ultimately face.

7.00 A game of Monopoly amongst the siblings has reached the argument stage and is abandoned. Some children are being pyjamad. Trevor's grandparents arrive and comforting tea is brewed. Adam's family tuck into pizzas.

7.50 The cinema trip returns. "It was brill." The long day staff leave.

8.45 As more children are put to bed the shift begins to wind down. A bed is made up for the Grandad and Grandma who are already proving to be pillars of strength. Socks and pants are gathered up for the laundry. Notes are written up and the night staff, fare-welled thirteen hours ago, are greeted back.

10.50 The twilight-shift member peels chunky chips for the two cinema-trip boys reluctantly admitting their tiredness. Grandad returns an empty tea tray to the kitchen. He is too exhausted but needs a quarter of an hour to unload his pain and grief not only for Trevor but for his daughter and son-in-law. The chip making is suspended to accommodate one of the most important parts of the job- listening and being alongside.

1.30am All seems quiet. The hub-bub of the day has gone. The night staff tip toe their corridor patrol, gently whispering assurance to those whose sleep is broken by pain or dreams. A tiny hand in bigger hand is led bleary-eyed to the loo. A teddy "lost overboard" is retrieved and reunited with its snuggling owner.

2.10 A buzzer stabs the silence and a red light directs staff to a child with muscular dystrophy. Locked in his immobility he asks to be rolled over on to his other side.

2.50 A Mum appears on the corridor ostensibly for some Paracetamol but really for reassurance and spends 20 minutes in gentle talk and comfort until she too is hugged and returns to her bedroom, hopefully to succumb to sleep.

3.05 The seconds, minutes and hours are ticking by. Feed pumps whirr their gentle rhythm backed by the humming and hissing of ventilator machines alongside the sound of whimpering sleep and talking dreams.

3.45 Tomorrow's veg is peeled and sliced ready for Robin's arrival. It is time for the mid-shift ritual of a sneak raid on the fridge for a tasty morsel and one of Carol's tray bake cakes. The microwave pings announcing their snack is ready and the night staff can rest for a little while, but strategically place themselves where they can still keep a finely tuned ear to the sound and movement of every bedroom.

4.50 The kitchen is spic and span, the settee cushions are plumped up; the playroom tidied. Abandoned toys are reunited – Lego with Playmobile, Chance with Community Chest, Batman with Robin, the engine with its carriages. A new day is prepared for.

5.35   The screeching tawny owl makes its last sortie quartering the garden as its night too draws to a close.

6.00   The ironing board is folded away at last. Outside the back door the milkman oblivious to the quiet of the houses whistles as he makes his early delivery.

6.20   The faint streaks of dawn are colour washed against the sky. Fatigue is rescued by a final coffee, but tired eyes must still write up notes from the night.

7.10   The crunch of wheels on gravel heralds the arrival of the day shift. Car doors again clunk the ritual of arrival. The back door latch clicks and squeaks open as the first "early" comes along the corridor. "Good night?" – "Yes, not bad at all." The dark hours have safely passed. A new day begins.

special adventures and everyday stories

When I asked members of the care team, parents and children about what to include to give a flavour of the House there were certain recurring themes. Special trips and occasions were mentioned a lot; so to give a flavour of the fun and the planning that go into these outings Linda Foley has put together people's rememberings of trips to the seaside. Alison Ward talks about how a straight forward shopping trip can turn into quite an occasion when she is navigating. A particularly memorable happening was Christmas Eve 2007 when the garden was turned into a winter wonderland, and this is recalled by Linda Hedley, together with Dr Sam Browning. Another recurring theme is the very popular visits of the various animals to Martin House; the children's enjoyment of these is described by Ginny Barker. Something of the magic of the popular 'themed days' is captured by Lesley Clements, a talented spontaneous story teller, in the story she wove after watching her son Alex playing during a 'Knights and Princesses' themed day. Another parent with a gift for story telling is Liz Varley, and she shares something of her family's story through her 'tale of two sharks'. A father, David Bond, wrote a poem after a restorative family stay about what he fondly refers to as 'Rainbow House'.

Also important are just normal days and Helen Scouller talks about the myriad things that make up a 'normal' day at Martin House. Louise Taylor remembers one particular family visit and how much she valued just being able to relax and watch her children playing happily without feeling any pressure to join in. Things many of us take for granted can also be very special and Sandy Johnston recalls the importance to her son Calum of his daily walk in the garden during the last week of his life.

This chapter ends with contributions reflecting some of the thoughts and feelings of the children and young people themselves. Cath Knowles reflects on how children deal with sad and difficult times. Wil Warren talks about the peace that her daughter, Kirsty, found at Martin House and how she felt safe and understood there. In the pieces from Kay Gadsby we get a powerful sense of her story and the awareness and understanding that children can bring to what is happening. In the poem that J Spratt wrote on the very morning he died we marvel at the wisdom of our children.

"...beside the seaside, beside the sea": Linda Foley

On lovely sunny days the opportunity lends itself to take the children on trips further a field. It has to be said the planning and organisational skills can be a challenge but a very worth while one when you see the joy on the children's faces. To make it happen the team has to work together, the night staff preparing a yummy picnic, the cars filled with petrol and sorted, all the things required for the day, the all important buckets and spades, camera, sunscreen and towels as well as the practical and necessary supplies of medicines, special feeds, back up ventilator, suction machines, spare batteries, oh and the kitchen sink!

A favourite outing is to the seaside, some of the children and families have never been and those that have love the opportunity to go again. Having a child with a life limiting illness in the family can sometimes curtail the normal family outings that other families enjoy and this can be a wonderful opportunity to fulfil some of those activities. On one occasion a trip to Bridlington included a picnic and a play on the beach, some of the children ran ahead with Bren to make a large boat out of sand. Salma shaking with excitement couldn't wait to get her cossie on so she could go paddling and jumping over the waves with Sarah.

Little Freddie, who recently had been in hospital for a very long time, just loved dangling his feet in the sea, helped by Chris. After a couple of happy hours playing on the beach, the bouncy castle, ball pool and ice creams beckoned then it was time for home.

A trip to Scarborough with a family who had never been to the seaside made it an extra special outing. Approaching the sea, the windows were wound down and Abi shouted, what's that noise? It was the seagulls squawking overhead; passing the amusement arcades she wanted to know why a man was calling out numbers – bingo was something else that was new to her.

When they finally arrived at the beach everyone piled out, for those in wheelchairs access is always a bit difficult to get close to the sea but everyone managed. Abi especially wanted to get the most out of this her first experience of the sea. She asked "can I smell it"? "Of course". "Can I feel it?", "course you can", "can I taste it"?!!
Bren on the care team sums up so well what it means to the team to be able to facilitate trips like this for the children and families.

" the feeling we got was indescribable, an amazing experience seeing something as familiar to us through a young person's eyes. She made us listen, smell and feel the beach".

Caring and working alongside this fantastic group of children and young people opens our eyes to a kaleidoscope of experiences giving us new colours and different ways of viewing the world through their eyes.

Dreaming of a white Christmas!: Linda Hedley

It is the stuff of films, Christmas cards and dreams; to see families coming together at Christmas time to have fun in a snowy wonderland! For the families and care team at Martin house this dream did come true on Christmas Eve 2007, all thanks to the generosity of a local businessman who donated tons of artificial snow to us after successfully bidding for it on an internet auction site.

In the past we have not always made a huge event out of Christmas as we are aware that for many families, for a variety of reasons, it is not always the happiest or easiest of times. We were, therefore, all very anxious about this day and hoped that it would be a success. We invited families who lived within easy travelling distance of Martin House and also the children of Martin House staff. Our biggest fear was that no one would come or that it would rain.

Christmas Eve arrived and it was not raining and by 8 a.m. the car park outside Martin house was filled with TV camera crews who had come to capture the scene. A lorry arrived and backed into the garden and a mountain of snow was tipped out – a wonderful army of volunteers from Xscape wheelbarrowed the snow into place in an area just outside the children's bedrooms. What a hive of activity…….fundraisers being interviewed, Robin and the housekeepers preparing the refreshments, the 'Petes' putting up extra decorations and lights and the library being transformed into Santa's grotto!! Still there was the anxiety of would anyone come? By 10 a.m. all was ready - the Martin House garden had been transformed into a winter wonderland – what an amazing sight! The first of the families were arriving and suddenly the air was filled with squeals of delight and laughter. For many of the children this was their first experience of snow but they certainly knew what to do with it – snowball fights abounded, encouraged and some would say instigated by the adults present. Children were taken out of their wheelchairs to sit on groundsheets on the snow to build snowmen whilst others enjoyed rides on sledges. It was difficult to decide who was enjoying this the most – the adults or the children? Amongst all this fun and frolics a special guest arrived straight from the North Pole. it was Santa!! After meeting many of the families he was invited into his grotto by the Christmas fairy, (known to some as Sheila our

Head of Care) where the children visited him to tell him of any last minute wishes. They each received a gift and an opportunity to have their photo taken with Santa.

By 12.30 the families were leaving, the TV crews had gone, Santa had many more pressing engagements to fulfil and it began to rain!

It is difficult to put into words how special it had been. Those of us who were working that day felt that it was the best start to Christmas that any of us could have wished for and what a privilege it had been to be part of such a wonderful experience. It highlighted to all of us the important role Martin House can play in offering the children and their families the opportunity to experience joy, laughter and fun and to add to the store of happy memories.

Sam Browning

Xmas eve last year was a special day. It is one of the fun memories that will stay with me for ever. Tonnes and tonnes of snow had been donated to Martin House, and we were invited along with the families that visit us to enjoy a festive time. I can't remember the last time we had a real white Christmas. It was fantastic.

I was struck by the generosity of the local business man who had donated the snow, the kindness of the hard working helpers who wheeled barrow after barrow of it to the area of the garden we were using, the large number of our families who came specially for the occasion and the sheer joy on the children's faces. As he always does, Robin had put on some festive refreshment. There was festive music, a Father Christmas and lots and lots of silliness in the snow. I include myself and my own children in that last comment. It was lovely to see everyone, able and not so able, let their hair down and have fun.

I think the occasion summed up Martin House for me- it was heart warming, safe, child and family centred, slightly unusual and brought huge smiles to the faces of everyone there. It showed the generosity of people towards Martin House and felt like a bit of a thank you to all the amazing families we meet for all that they teach us. It is a unique privilege to be a small part of Martin House.

Trips out: **Alison Ward**

Since starting to work at Martin House I have been on numerous trips out with the children to various places, including shopping at McArthur Glen Designer Centre in York and Meadowhall in Sheffield, visiting the bird garden at Harewood House and the farm at Temple Newsam and going to play at Crazy Tykes indoor play arena.

There are many stories to tell from these trips but one I particularly remember was a trip to the Designer Centre with Summer, (one of the children who visit Martin House) and Pam. Summer likes to take it easy in the morning when staying at Martin House and tends to get up at 11am or thereabouts, but due to our trip Summer was up by 9.30am and we were in the vehicle, down the motorway and indicating to come off as we had seen the sign for the Designer Centre by 10.15am.

To get to the Designer Centre from the motorway a few roundabouts need to be negotiated. At this stage I hasten to add that Pam was driving and I was co-pilot. We managed to negotiate the first and second roundabouts smoothly, but when it came to the third roundabout we went round it twice and a final time for good luck even though I was clearly stating left at the appropriate moment. Summer thought this was hilarious and to be honest so did Pam and I. Once we had managed the roundabouts we had to locate the disabled parking and after many speed bumps and giggles from Summer we found the appropriate area and a space. The shopping could begin.

We went in lots of shops and Summer seemed quite keen on a variety of items, but in the end she decided to buy a bracelet which she put on immediately she had bought it. After a couple of hours of shop after shop we had a drink in a café where we chatted about our trip before heading home. The homeward journey went very smoothly and we were back in time for a late lunch. Summer showed off her bracelet to everybody and then she went to have a well deserved rest on her bed.

I spent a lot of time with Summer during this visit and I believe she found me quite amusing- she often laughed out loud, especially at my tendency to want to get her up early and try to fit in as many activities as possible during the days of her stay.

Animals at Martin House: Ginny Barker

Martin House is a building which is bursting with so much diversity, each day is so different and unpredictable. Fun is something which happens a lot at Martin House and to help contribute to this special and important part of the house environment is our access to animals and the importance they bring to the hospice, touching the poorly child, sisters and brothers, parents and staff in some remarkable way.

The benefits that contact with animals bring include: reducing stress levels – just through stoking an animal; sensory experiences of smell and touch; confidence boosting; the responsibility of caring for the animals and of course just the pure enjoyment and fun. These are all so important for children. Communication between animal and child is absolutely magical to witness. The animals also help produce a calming atmosphere.

For many years Martin House has been fortunate to have contact with the local donkey centre. We are able to book sessions at the centre, held in the indoor, heated school, where both siblings and poorly children can experience riding on a donkey, grooming a donkey or perhaps having a ride in the donkey cart which is wheelchair friendly too. Some families ask as soon as they arrive for their planned stay, "Can we book a session at the donkey centre?," and enjoy going as a family during their stay.

Let me share some magic moments I have witnessed

 A few years ago we took two siblings 5 year old Thomas and 6 year old Jon to the donkey centre. It was Christmas week and Santa had his grotto at the centre. The boys were thrilled. Thomas is usually very active and quite challenging at times (his way of getting noticed), but during this outing he listened well to the staff, he was gentle towards the donkey and concentrated on riding. He entered the Grotto on the donkey looking very apprehensive but determined. On emerging through the Grotto his face was lit up, with a beaming smile, very rarely seen from this child. The care team who had taken the children felt their eyes fill with tears. During that session Thomas was a different little boy. The donkey had worked its magic and on returning back to Martin House both boys were able to talk to their parents about the outing.

The donkey centre also arranges visits to Martin House, on average two Tuesday morning sessions a month. The donkey comes to join us in the conservatory and sets the scene for a lovely calm time. Everyone has a smile on their face seeing the donkey inside. Harry was in the final stages of his illness and cuddled on his mum's knee, the donkey moved towards Harry and let his muzzle rest in Harry's hands, at this Harry lifted his head - what a special moment for both mum and Harry. 12 year old Jane, sitting in her wheelchair, was assisted to stroke the donkey; she became very vocal and started to stretch her fingers out on her own, a clear indication to feel the donkey again. These moments are so special.

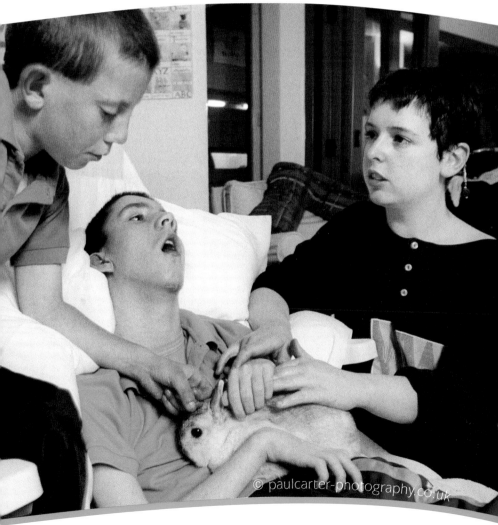

© paulcarter-photography.co.uk

Jonathan, a 6 year old who found it very difficult to communicate to others and needs a strict routine to help keep him calm, was taken into the conservatory to meet the donkey. He focused straight away on the donkey and stretched his hand out towards the animal. The change of routine didn't upset Jonathan. Donkey magic had struck again. These moments may last seconds or minutes, but they are precious moments with amazing impact.

Charles, aged 17 years, an electric wheelchair user, took the donkey around the garden, holding the end of the leading rope with assistance. Charles led the donkey over Tiger Bridge and up and down the paths. Charles was in control. He had the biggest smile on his face when explaining to others what he had done.

Martin House also has a close connection with a local small farm which takes in rescued animals. When a sibling group session is held (for children who have a poorly sibling accessing the hospice) the animals are booked to come to Martin House in the afternoon. The animals are always a great hit and when they arrive suddenly welly throwing, dangling doughnuts and football are forgotten. All we can see are goats taking children for walks! (Yes it should be the other way round!) Rabbits in felt hats, guinea pigs having grooming sessions and lambs being bottle fed. Laughter and smiles are seen amongst the children and yet this fun time is giving them so much value. Laura, 6 years old, always asks "….and are the animals coming?" as soon as she arrives for the sibling group.

The animal experience at Martin House gives such fun filled moments and long lasting memories.

Princess and a Knight: Lesley Clements

Sir Alex Knight of the Redroom was discussing his Action men team with Sir Bob, when they heard a scream. Sir Alex jumped onto his charger 'Discovery' and headed off towards the sound. By the Tiger Bridge he found Princess Ginny, who had fallen from her stead Fudge and grazed her leg. Sir Alex helped her on to the sturdy charger Discovery and took her back to the Redroom.

Meanwhile Sir Bob had called handmaiden Gertrude and holster Pete. On hearing what had happened holster Pete and his shadow Zak set off to capture and take care of Fudge. Handmaiden Gertrude fetched water to bathe Princess Ginny's leg and called for physician Mike to check her wound. Physician Mike examined Princess Ginny's leg and bandaged it, telling her to rest for a day or so and all would be well. At this moment Queen Jan appeared to check on her daughter's well being. Queen Jan was so pleased to find her doing well, she thanked Sir Alex for rescuing her daughter and called for chief chef Robin to prepare a feast in his honour. Empress Sheila sent invitations far and wide throughout the kingdom of West Yorkshire. Chef Robin set out to prepare a mighty feast. Maid Hilz started producing decorations, helpful and caring maid Olive swept the floor and spread new rushes. Minstral Mike got a band together. People came from far and wide and all had a wonderful party to honour Sir Alex and Princess Ginny. At the end Friar Mark gave a service of Thanksgiving in the chapel for a truly wonderful day.

A Tale of Two Sharks: Liz Varley

Isn't it funny, as soon as you say your newborn baby can have any of your soft toys but "that" one, they attach themselves to said soft toy. This is exactly what my first daughter Megan did. She obviously sensed Horris (my soft toy shark) was particularly special, and decided she couldn't live without him. After a few months of trying unsuccessfully to reclaim Horris, I decided I needed to find another. Thankfully I did. Feeling very pleased with myself I presented Megan with Horris' twin, Fluffy (so called because his fur was so fluffy and new). She took one look and turned her nose up at the imposter, pushing him away. Now what? Well, there was only one thing for it. The next two weeks saw me taking Horris and Fluffy to bed with me every night, making sure I hugged them both. Finally, Fluffy was no longer an imposter and was welcomed with open arms. Everyone was happy. I had Horris back, Megan had her own new shark, and Horris had a twin brother.

Life was going really well, until at eight months old we started to notice things with Megan that weren't right. The next ten months saw us backwards and forwards between hospitals, doctors and consultants. We lost count of all the blood tests when it got near a hundred. We couldn't keep track of all the other awful tests. Fluffy was her faithful servant, constantly there trying to help her cope. Horris was there too when tests were really awful. I think this was when Horris and Fluffy went from tea drinking sharks to drinking alcohol!

At seventeen months old Megan developed pneumonia and landed up in the LGI. This was when the trauma really started. Within a couple of weeks she had so many blood tests, x rays, NG tubes, a battery of other invasive tests and a gastrostomy fitted. We were also told, finally, that she had

a neurodegenerative disease, but they had no idea what. I was six months pregnant with our son, William, at the time, and was trying to keep stress to a minimum! I was going home with Horris at night while Dave stayed with Megan and Fluffy in hospital. Most mornings when I went in I would find Fluffy with his nose under the alcohol dispenser, apparently trying to calm himself. Neat alcohol in gel form seemed to be what an overly stressed Nurse shark needed to help him cope with seeing his owner in such a state. When things got really bad Horris and Fluffy would both be with Megan. As soon as the crisis was over the nurses would come in to find two nurse sharks with their noses under the alcohol dispenser.

Horris and Fluffy got up to all sorts during the two months we were in hospital. When they went down to theatre with Megan they had their own identification bands put on round their tails, each with their own names. The nurses always made sure Horris and Fluffy were ok as well as Megan, and always tucked them in with her when she was asleep. They threatened to bite the limbs off staff we didn't like, much to the nurses' amusement. They swam up and down the corridors and wards, hassled the nurses, drank tea and alcohol gel, and as an occasional treat got to eat fish in the canteen. Megan would only do physio if the therapists played with Horris and Fluffy. She point blank refused to do anything if the sharks weren't included.

After two months we finally got out of hospital. We had four weeks to the day till William was due. In that time we had to adapt to caring for Megan on our own with feed pumps, gastrostomies, a new chair, bath chair, apnoea alarm etc, sort out baby things for William and buy all the stuff we hadn't yet had chance to buy (including a double pushchair we hadn't anticipated). We had to get Megan used to Martin House, a place we'd never heard of until then, and get her over her extreme fear of other people, so we could leave her there on her own while Dave and I went to Jimmy's to have William. I was stressed. I couldn't see how we were going to achieve all that, specially as I was eight months pregnant and huge.

We walked in through Martin House doors and were completely engulfed by warmth and compassion. I knew it was a good place when one of the first things they asked was who the sharks were. Horris and Fluffy were happy when they realised there was an endless supply of tea, a large fish tank stocked with fish, and staff who cared as much about them as Megan. They also discovered Martin House has amazingly snuggly duvets, another of their passions.

After six days at Martin House a really nice lady called Barbara looked after Megan. Up to that point Megan had not really relaxed with the care team. Barbara adopted Horris and Fluffy as the larger than life characters they had become, and bingo, Megan loved being with her. The following week I went in to have William. It was a c-section so Megan was at Martin House for four days. Barbara looked after Megan, and by all accounts Megan and Fluffy had a whale (no pun intended!) of a time. I had Horris with me, and every day Dave would bring Megan for a few hours before going back to Martin House. Fluffy would recount so many tales of things he and Megan had been getting up to with the staff, including chasing the fish in the fish tank. Barbara, Megan and Fluffy even made William a fantastic card with a shark on it signed from Megan and Fluffy. Fluffy took advantage of the alcohol gel dispenser every time they visited.

© Liz Varley

A few months later things were settling down to a strange kind of normal. I had managed to get Horris back and Megan was happy with Fluffy, and occasionally Horris too. Then William decided he wanted Horris. Poor Horris, he wasn't cut out to be so popular. Woolworths had stopped selling his brothers a long while before, so the hunt was on for another shark. I spent so many nights on the internet shark hunting. Eventually I found one. It was completely different, but William loved Sydney anyway. However, he only loved him at night. He has always preferred Horris by day. So now Horris and Fluffy were a permanent feature of family life. As long as they were getting into trouble it made Megan and William laugh. They chased fish at garden centres, tickled and drank tea in cafes, snuggled into the footmuff when in the pushchair, became the stars of all the family videos (much to Megan's amusement) and generally misbehaved.

Megan had two more chest infections which resulted in hospitalisation, the second of which proved fatal. After several weeks on intensive care, with Megan very ill and on the ventilator, there was nothing more anyone could do. Dave was due to run the Great North Run for Martin House, and having just discovered we would be taking Megan to Martin House probably where she would die in a few days, we were faced with a huge decision. We desperately wanted to raise money, so some of my friends helped me care for Megan and a six month old William while Dave went and ran. It was very scary and very emotional. One of my closest friends had at the last minute got us a six foot inflatable shark that looked just like Fluffy. Megan needed the real Fluffy, so Dave strapped giant Fluffy on his back and got him round all thirteen miles for Megan. It must have touched something in people as Dave managed to raise just over £8000, we were staggered. Just four days later we took Megan to Martin House and off the ventilator. She lived for seventeen hours till it all became too much and she died the following morning, Fluffy by her side. After a short while she was taken to the little room where she had all her favourite things. Fluffy was tucked up with her under an under the sea duvet that the staff had found for her. There he stayed looking after Megan for the last time, before her funeral. He was there with Megan for nine days, while I clung to Horris and generally made him soggy. We arranged the funeral with a huge amount of help from the staff. We managed to find a coffin covered in a sea scape, and had someone design a Horris and Fluffy to go on the top. Without even speaking to us they managed to capture their personalities perfectly. The florist pulled off a huge

Fluffy brilliantly, and Megan was put in the coffin holding a photo of Horris and Fluffy. It was a sad reunion, however, when Horris and Fluffy came together again; before we took Megan to the church they had one last play with Megan, sliding up and down the coffin.

Life has been hard since then, but William adopted Fluffy and had both sharks for a while. Fluffy wasn't loved like Megan loved him, but William has had them doing all sorts. He insisted on them being fed tea, porridge, fish and a whole host of other things. He's carried them everywhere, made them chase fish at The Deep, tucked them up under blanky (their blanket), snuggled them, changed their nappies and sat them on his potty (even though he still refuses), and got them into trouble at every opportunity. All his story books have to be about sharks and the characters' names changed to Fluffy and Horris. It's amazing how much a toddler can blame on a pair of cheeky sharks!

Seven months after Megan died I fell pregnant with Ellie. We don't know if either William or Ellie have the same condition as Megan so the pregnancy this time was more of a worry. Needless to say we were at the hospital a lot so Horris and Fluffy were once again let loose on the alcohol gel.
Ellie was finally born on new year's eve. Within a week she had attached herself to Fluffy and refused to go to sleep without him. William reluctantly had to give him up and be with happy with just Horris. Ellie and Fluffy have become inseparable and he is once again extremely well loved. I have never seen a baby attach itself to anything so young, and I can only think it's Megan's way of looking after her baby sister. It's amazing how two sharks have made a strong link between all three siblings, even though Megan died before Ellie was born. William loves seeing photos of Megan with Fluffy. Not bad considering Horris was never going to be for the baby!

For the last two years we have attended a memorial service at Martin House for all the families who have lost children. Everyone wears name badges, and every year somebody has written badges out for Horris and Fluffy too, without a word from us. William loves the fact they have badges, and this year has learnt to read their names as a result.

We have come across people since Megan died that we dealt with when she was alive. The funny thing is they only ever recognise us from the sharks, and always remember Fluffy's name. We couldn't have got through everything we have without the enormous support and love from Martin House, and the humour and silliness from Horris and Fluffy. So if you're ever out and about and see a family with a couple of well loved sharks getting up to mischief, you can be sure it will be Horris and Fluffy!

© Liz Varley

An Ode to Martin House: Dave Bond

There is a house
Not in the skies
Or heavens above
But over the rainbow
This house full of love
It's a special house
I think you should know
For special children
It's where they can go
Where special people
Look after their needs
Along with the birds
That sing in the trees
So pack up your bags
And off you go
To the house
Full of colours
Over the rainbow

Normal days at Martin House: Helen Scouller

I've tried to think about a myriad of things that are typical of a day at Martin House. There are many events that I can remember:

-   A particular trip to the seaside long ago; a convoy to Scarborough with a huge picnic assembled at the crack of dawn. We did the beach, the Sea Life Centre and ice creams, maybe chips too, but I can recall most clearly the trip home. I had to be reminded by Bernadette to slow down on the hills because the lads in the back were struggling to keep their balance, then we had to practise her Spanish, for her language class that evening, with three, five and seven year olds helping ....'mi amo'.......

-   We've had some great treasure hunts outside: me, unable to remember where I've hidden the answers; everyone else, children in push chairs, youngsters whizzing in electric wheelchairs (sometimes with a brother and sister on board), siblings, parents, team, running to the far reaches of the garden. These treasure hunts always seem to involve me bellowing on the grass mound at various people – I think I am meant to be helping.

-   I once had to follow a cross sibling (he had argued with his brother) through the garden asking him to stop. He didn't, he jumped over the gate and carried on up the road apace. I tried to open the gate, realised I too had to climb over it and get on with catching him up. I only managed to prevent a full on hike to Bradford by asking him to stop because I'd had to scale a fence, run and was out of breath, just for him!

-   I remember helping a brother and sister write and decorate two letters to their brother who had just died. They were very simple – just questions – like they were chatting and wanting to know all was well. They placed these in the coffin.

-   We've had mornings in the art room with lots of children and team, making, painting, sticking and chatting, often with some of the most profoundly disabled youngsters responding to jokes and making choices between two colours or shapes or which pop star is most fanciable.

- We once invited my friend Tony to show us how to decorate clay tiles. The table was pulled away from the wall, children on all sides, standing room only. As a teacher, he knew how to get the best out of everyone – they were beautiful, spare objects.

- When we've painted the mural in Martin House with the children and parents, it's fantastic to see how proud they are with the results. One youngster was able to reach up high because her electric wheelchair could be elevated – she painted her insect so carefully.

- I loved the time Father Christmas arrived by helicopter. I was with a young man from the Lodge who I've known a long time. (We once went to the pub together where he decided to kiss a young man who stood aside to let him have a shot at pool). He wanted to greet Santa Claus, get inside the helicopter, put a helmet on and then go and bake biscuits. I suggested we wait for the helicopter to leave. When the motor started and blades went round and round and this huge hunk of metal lifted off the ground it was one of the most amazing things I have ever seen. Then I baked shortbread.

- I sat with a lad in the Lodge for a couple of hours, at the table, while I drew and executed a piece of peelable 'window art' that he described and had me alter to his specifications. We talked about significant things and laughed about something that ended in him producing a poster on the computer advertising me as a hitman – I can't recall how we got there.

- I had a very quiet time once with a six year old who wanted to paint a picture of his teddy, and talk about all sorts, while I finished decorating plates and tiles with a baby's footprints on for her parents who wanted to treasure these special memories of her. Half an hour later I was describing this scene to a group of foreign visitors as they had a look around the House, wanting to know about a typical example of my work.

- These are specific events and yet they're also everyday. Our families provide us with much stimulation and challenges, we hopefully help them be in the present and create memories because there is no 'typical' for them.

A week at martin House: **Louise Taylor**

There are so many memories of our time at Martin House that I could probably write a book myself. We started to visit when Jack was nearly two and our family grew over the years to include Joe and Lucy too. As for many families our memories include laughter, joy, tears and heartbreak but throughout all of those love!

I have decided to share some of my memories of a very special week we spent at Martin House in the summer of 2002. Our family was complete, Jack was well and we were all enjoying a lovely summer.

sitting in the sun

On our first morning we eventually woke up to discover the children had long before been taken out. As every Martin House parent knows sleep is a precious gift and the knowledge that the responsibility had been lifted meant that we hadn't woken until late. However when you are used to three or four hours sleep (if you are lucky) and you have seven or eight, you wake up feeling like you have the hangover from hell. So after being made coffee and toast, out to the garden we went for a lay in the sun. I had a Harry Potter book and read and read and read. It was the first time in years that I finished a book.

As always the whole house knew that my children had arrived back in the house due to Jack's loud choruses of "I'm Back !! ". They had had a fabulous time and for the rest of the day we enjoyed watching them play. We didn't need to do anything. Even the dreaded shout of, "I'm poohed" was dealt with by the wonderful care team of the day, as were drugs, baths, cutting up of food, clearing up of mess etc, etc, etc.
A complete rest. Perfect.

water

As we were enjoying lovely hot sunny weather(in summer for once), water inevitably made frequent appearances that week. The big slide had been strategically placed in a large paddling pool so that the children could slide down and splash in. Fantastic fun, I have wonderful memories of the boys running back round to the steps with their soaking wet nappies flapping round their knees ready for another go. Joseph, helped by Chris, washed the little tykes car on the mosaic in the Lavender garden with a hosepipe. Both of them were absolutely soaked.

One of my favourite memories during that time is of a waterfight they had. In true Martin House style they didn't use supersoakers, water pistols or any conventional waterfighting equipment. All the children were playing with syringes. A definite taboo in "normal "circles, indeed a parent's worst nightmare but excellent for water fights especially the big ones used for feeding! My husband and I were sitting on a bench watching this happen. Whilst we thoroughly enjoyed the fun and the laughter we didn't need to join in and nobody asked us to. This is so precious when you are exhausted. Dr Mike was talking to a parent near the house, just out of firing range, and kept glancing over his shoulder. As Helen bent down to rearm from a bucket of water Jack scored a fantastic hit right down the front of her cleavage. I can hear the laughter that one produced in my head now as I am writing this.

Suddenly, with his usual good sense of timing, Dr Mike, without further ado, abandoned the parent and joined in. After being chased around the garden by Joseph and given a good soaking he returned to the waiting parent as if nothing had happened.

Only at Martin House.

The Barbeque

Summer is always full of invitations to BBQs but not many to a BBQ at the home of Lord and Lady Halifax. Martin House had received an invitation so off we went. We set off in convoy and after a while we began the long drive down the driveway of the house through fields and fields until eventually arriving at the house.

It was a privilege to experience spending time with this truly lovely couple. We ate our food looking over rolling fields chatting with Lord Halifax in the shade of his summer house. He lent the children his big sun hats. We ate ice cream with home made cookies. Lady Halifax introduced us all to her pet pig, which the children thought was hysterical. After lunch, Vicky and Chris took the children into their pool whilst we sat dangling our feet in the beautiful cool water. This was a magical day we will never forget.

Memories

Our son Jack died at Martin house on Christmas Eve 2005, much sooner than any one had expected. To lose a child is a devastating experience and there are many dark and desperate days to be got through. Memories of happy fun times at Martin house are one of the things that can see us through and help us to remember the wonderful times we shared with our little boy. Thank you Martin House for everything.

Calum's daily walk: Sandy Johnston

Our son had such an aggressive illness, no one really knew what was happening despite all their best efforts, but what was clear was that we were losing him, not just physically but himself too. Calum had always been a fighter, gutsy and determined to succeed at whatever he did but now he was withdrawing, turning to the wall in his hospital bed and no longer communicating.

We were desperate and when one of the doctor's suggested we try a break for a few days at Martin House, despite being extremely anxious about the idea, we agreed to give it a go. The atmosphere from the start was amazing; calm, relaxed, sensitive but also full of hope...not at all like the stereotype you might imagine. Nothing was too much trouble and when Calum indicated on his first morning that he might like to try going out into the garden the care team made it happen. It became an important part of his routine every morning. It took more than an hour to get everything ready, his equipment, and himself all wrapped up, but he got so very much pleasure from it. It was as if he reconnected with life and the rhythm of life in that garden. He did it with us every day, right up until the day before he died.

© Bryony Wright

© Bindy Pease

Learning from the children: Cath Knowles

I have worked at Martin House for four years and I never fail to be amazed at the diversity of what happens here, of the resilience of the children and families and of the supportive nurturing presence that Martin House affords families and staff alike.

But something that has made me really stop and think, is how children and teenagers can teach us, as adults, so much about living life and how to deal with whatever it throws at you. I've been interested in this particularly through spending time with the siblings of the children who use Martin House. I see how they express and deal with sad and difficult times by dipping in and out of a feeling and balancing it with other things, like play or an activity. They don't feel guilty about doing that and it seems a very healthy and restorative way of balancing their sadness without it even being a conscious process.

One such occasion that highlighted this for me was after a young girl had died at Martin House. Her family were staying with her, Mum and three brothers. On the day of the funeral the two younger brothers were very upset and chose not to attend the service, so they stayed at Martin House. I was looking after them and we sat having a hug and talking about their sister. At the time that her service was taking place we went over to the chapel to light some candles.

The two boys had made friends with three other children who were staying at the House, and they wanted to come and help light the candles as well. It was genuinely warming to see how supportive the other children were to the boys and how the boys seemed to find comfort in that support. One of the youngsters who was at Martin House for a respite visit suggested that he read a piece from the Qu'ran, but his sister informed us that none of us were allowed to touch the Qu'ran. After pondering this problem she came up with the solution that if she held the book with her sleeves pulled over her hands, she could then give the book to her brother who could handle it. She informed us that it would be acceptable for him to hold it because he was in a wheelchair. So her brother turned the pages and she read the text. After the reading they all wanted to play a game, so we played a very boisterous game of musical chairs. During the game, 'music Mike' came to the chapel to deliver a message. He ended up joining us and started off a guessing game that everyone enjoyed. The time in the chapel ended with an energetic and excitable game of tig with Mike providing the music on the keyboard.

A day at Martin House feels a lot like how children deal with sadness, with that dipping in and out of different feelings, situations and activities, combined with the restorative support and encouragement that you are provided by your colleagues.

our last few days together: **Wil Warren**

You kept repeating, 'I love you' over and over again. It has been such a long time since you were able to speak clearly.

That night you started fitting, you never regained consciousness in between. I knew you were desperately ill but I knew you did not want to go to hospital. I rang the doctor, who was unable to do anything else but send you to hospital. The ambulance came, they insisted on putting a drip into you but they were unable to do so. They put you in the ambulance and tried again, but to no avail. Finally we drove away in the early morning traffic with the sirens blaring. How you would have loved that.

At the hospital they managed to get a drip in, and when I was allowed to see you, you were looking a lot better, but your whole body showed your unhappiness. You were so angry with me for sending you there. You remained in hospital for a few days; they were very sad and miserable days. Then it was almost as if the sun had come out in your cold room- you had a visitor from Martin House. Oh what a difference that made; this all embracing warmth, comfort and such sincere smiles.

You finally were able to convince those in authority you knew what you wanted and were so prepared for the consequences that they let you go. An ambulance took us but they lost the way. We did not care, we were going where we wanted to be. When we finally entered Martin House the utter relief we both felt; we were embraced by the warmth and comfort and we felt so safe. It was the same feeling that we had both experienced on our first visit. We had seen so many dismal places and here we were, in this lovely safe haven. You felt you had come home, the one place you wanted to spend your last few days.

We had some wonderful days with you, and all the staff. You did know what was going to happen, but you were happy, you had your wish. Even Bob, our next door neighbour's dog, was happy to just sit on your bed; something he would never have done before.

Finally it was time for you to go.
You went peacefully.

We miss you still so very much. You are still all around us. From the moment you died until now you are with us in spirit. The greatest gift you gave me is your spirit still always with me. The greatest gift Martin House has given all of us left behind is the knowledge that you could die in peace, as you wanted it.

My real life Story, I'm a fighter: **Kay Gadsby**

My Real Life Story began just before my seventh birthday in January 1994.

I came home from school one day just after the start of term, after the Christmas holidays. My left knee was hurting me, and I told my mum and dad. They gave me some calpol to try and stop the pain. It worked for a few days but then I came home again in pain. My mum and dad asked me if I had fallen at school, and I said 'no', so they decided to take me to see the doctor, who said it was just 'growing pains.'By the way I am a majorette, and have been since the age of six. All the time that I had the pain I carried on training with the majorettes, and well, to cut a very long story short, mum and dad kept taking me to the doctors and they kept saying different things; for example, torn ligaments, fluid on the knee and also arthritis. This was from January to April 1994.

Then one Thursday night when mum and dad came to paick me up from training, Mrs Bailley who runs La Classique Majorettes in Wakefield, said to my dad that he should take me to the Accident and Emergency Unit because I couldn't do anything at training. So they took me to Pinderfields Hospital in Wakefield. There they did an X ray on my left leg and asked my parents if they could take me back to the fracture clinic the next day. They took me back the next day and did another X ray and told my mum and dad the worst thing that they could ever hear. The doctor said that he was 99.9% sure that I had cancer, and he thought I should go to the Royal Orthopaedic Hospital in Birmingham to have a biopsy to see if it was benign or malignant.

I was taken there on the Sunday for a week. There they did more X rays and scans, and then MRI-CT bone scans and all sorts. They then took me to theatre for a biopsy. The next ten days were the worst days of mum and dad's life. On the tenth day after the biopsy our GP came round to our house to tell my mum and dad that the results had come back and that I had cancer of the bone (osteosarcoma) and that they were to take me to St James' Hospital in Leeds, where I was to start an intensive course of chemotherapy, six doses in all.

After the first dose I started to lose my hair, and after the fourth dose I had to go back to Birmingham for an operation to remove two tumours that I had on my left leg. There they told me that they would have to take my left leg off from the top, and all I said was, 'Will I still be able to do majorettes?' They said that I would in time. The next morning, Thursday August 4th 1994, I went down to theatre for an operation. When I awoke the next day I found they had saved my leg by taking all the bone out and putting in a solid gold and titanium bone.

After intensive physiotherapy I went back to St James' Hospital for more chemotherapy. After the last one the doctor at St James' said that the chemotherapy had damaged some of my internal organs, my heart and my kidneys and also my hearing. They said that I should go to a hospital in Newcastle, the Freeman Heart Hospital. There I spent another week in hospital having an assessment for a heart transplant. After this I was told they were not prepared to do one because of my kidneys, so my mum and dad thought I was going to die. This was the week before Christmas 1994.

Although my chemotherapy had finished I still had to go to St James' every week for blood tests. Then in November 1997 a doctor told my mum and dad that I was getting worse and they didn't think I would live much longer. My dad asked the doctor, 'What about a heart and kidney transplant, because doctors can do heart and lung transplants.' The doctor said my chance of survival would probably be about 5 to 10% but I went back to Newcastle again and the doctors said they were willing to give it a try. This was in May 1998. I was given a bleeper, and in July 1998 I was given a chance for a whole new life. I had a heart and kidney transplant in Freeman Hospital in Newcastle.

Now six months later I am doing really good, still doing my majoretting and back at school, thanks to some very kind people.

(Written Aged 12 years)

Kay's Story

My story's sad but very true,
How my old heart made me blue.
I couldn't play or run around,
Until a match could be found.
Four and a half years on a waiting list
Wondering if I'd been missed.
Then one day a phone call came
With the organs that bore my name.
So to the Freeman I must go,
In an ambulance that was not slow.
I was nervous, full of fear
When that day was finally here.
Ward 23 was my destination
Where I would get my transplantation.
A heart and a kidney is what I received,
Now it's all over, boy I'm relieved.
Now I'm pink, that's never been known,
I cant wait to show the people back home.
I can only thank but never repay,
All that people did for me that day.
The doctors and nurses on Ward 23
A great big kiss for you from me.
As for those on Ward 28,
All I can say is you looked after me great.
Last but not least my own Dr Gibbs
Without whom I'd have gone insane,
As doctors go you're simply the best
In a different league to all the rest.
I've got carried away and must sign off
As the physio's coming to make me cough.

By Kay Gadsby and Berry

A Letter From Me In Heaven: **Kay Gadsby**

To my dearest Mum and Dad, something I'd like to say
But first of all to let you know that I arrived OK.
I'm writing this from Heaven, here I dwell with God above
Here there's no more tears of sadness
Here is just eternal love.

Please do not be unhappy just because I'm out of sight,
Remember that I'm with you every morning, noon and night.
That day I had to leave you when my life on earth was through
God picked me up and hugged me, He said, 'I welcome you.
It's good to have you back again; you were missed while you were gone.
As for your nearest and dearest they'll be here later on.
I need you badly, you are part of my plan
There's so much that we have to do to help our mortal man.'

God gave me a list of things that He wished for me to do
And foremost on my list was to watch and care for you.
And when you lie in bed at night, the day's chorus put to right
God and I are closest to you…in the middle of the night.

When you think of my life on earth, and all thosing loving years
Because you are only human these are bound to bring you tears.
But do not be afraid to cry, it does relieve the pain
Remember there would be no flowers unless there was some rain.
I wish that I could tell you all that God has planned
But if I were to tell you, you wouldn't understand.
But one thing is for certain, though my life on earth is o'er,
I'm closer to you now than ever I was before

There are many rocky roads ahead of you and many a hill to climb,
But together we can do it by taking one day at a time.
It was always my philosophy and I'd like it for you too…
That as you give unto the world, the world will give to you.
If you can help someone who's in sorrow and in pain,
Then you can say to God at night,'My day was not in vain.'

And now I am contented, that my life has been worthwhile
Knowing as I passed along the way, I made somebody smile.
So if you meet somebody who is sad and feeling low,
Just lend a hand to pick them up, as on your way you go.

When you're walking down the street, and you've got me on your mind,
I'm walking in your footsteps,
Only half a step behind.
And when it's time for you to go…
From that body to be free,
Remember you're not going
You're coming here to me.

LOVE YOU ALWAYS

Georgina Gadsby

One day I`ll see you again
and it will be as if we`ve never been apart.

All the anguish
All the pain
All the longing of my heart
will melt away and you`ll be there.
You`ll clasp my hand
and then at last we`ll understand
the wonder and the strength of love.

Sweetheart my eyes look up above this day,
and you are not very far away.

Love Mum and Dad

Get a life: J Spratt

Transforming mortality,
Accepting death
A true way to become alive.
Many sufferers of potentially terminal disease
Speak of an unshackling from those aspects of
Their life which had in the past tied them down
Into a lifestyle which was not truly theirs, or
Making them truly happy. Their confrontation with
Death was the key to new beginnings and possibilities.
Often this realization, and acting on the realization
Was enough to allow the patient to live, and live...
Surely these are lessons for us all, are you truly alive?
Don't wait until you're dead, get a life...

artists in residence

Representation for individuals

Maximising ability

Enabling Lodge

Being somebodies hands

Australia Day

One to one

Group

Poorly child

Parents

Along side

Thank you presents

Siblings

Keepsake

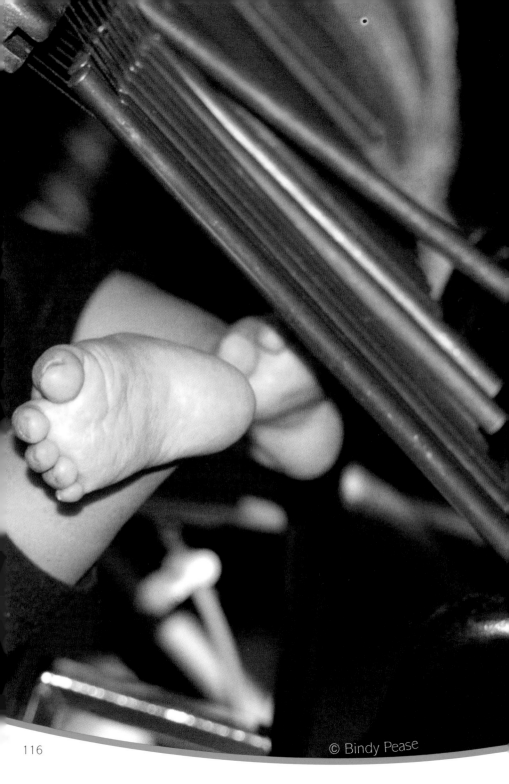

The role of music

"You must have the best job in the world," is a comment that we on the music team regularly receive from families as well as from people outside Martin House. This is maybe a reflection and perception of our role in the music therapy team. There is often a sense of fun in our music around the House, such as when we have an impromptu group session in the lounge or conservatory; poorly children, siblings, families and care team members, some relaxed, others frustrated wannabee pop idols.

It is the impromptu and unstructured nature of these events that makes our musicmaking so special. They evoke those spontaneous responses from all of us, allowing us to be expressive in small ways or to be as big a part of the session as we feel we want to be. Some are tuneful and delicate, some shy and tentative, others just loud and bossy!

It is also how as individuals we react to the involvement of others that in turn influences our own subsequent involvement. Sometimes it may be that another's confident approach gives us a green light to become more adventurous in sound or singing. Conversely it may be that we allow others to take the lead, ourselves in turn assuming the role of more supportive members of the group. On the other hand, those who find it difficult to be as actively involved may need a helping hand to achieve more, whether that be physical assistance or more motivational and musical guidance, whilst still experiencing that crucial supportive environment.

working and playing together in groups

The field of communication between all of those in a group is extremely complicated and intense. As well as the vocal and verbal aspects, the communication is also evident in numerous non verbal forms:

- Visual – including levels of eye contact, facial expressions, body language, positioning
- Auditory – including how loud or quiet someone might be playing
- Tactile – sensory perception, vibrations and sensory monitoring/ exploration of physical instruments.

Reading this we might think that how we participate and react in a big musical group or exchange is actually a fairly accurate guide or reflection of our everyday interactions and preferences. The beauty of creative media, and in this instance music, is how it allows us to be a little more 'honest' and natural with ourselves and in our interpersonal exchanges. The music becomes the central focus, whether or not we as professionals take a more passive role (listening and observing), and the emphasis can shift away from the conscious defensive behaviour that we might otherwise show when the interaction is more focused on verbal exchange.

Individual time

Away from the noise and fun in the more public arena of the lounge, there are special moments in theprivate space of the music room, bedrooms, light room and chapel. Taking all of these processes into what is the very

© Bindy Pease

intimate nature of a one to one session, means that the communication processes are narrowed down to the two individuals involved. However although only two people are involved, the level of focus is not less - if anything the interaction becomes more intensified. This type of setting allows even greater concentration on the interpersonal exchanges and individual idiosyncrasies that occur between those involved. Some individuals may feel more freedom to be actively involved in this setting and as a result feel a little more special in the process.

Similarly the private space allows there to be silence – an often underutilised commodity. There is time to allow individuals to engage and respond and initiate at their own pace. We are very lucky in our role to have the opportunity as clinicians to utilise such concepts and to support individuals as they engage at their own pace, and in their own way. Equally this is also the fundamental basis of the supportive element of our work.

Exploration of feelings

At a time of loss, fear or anxiety, it can be the supportive actions of a good listener or comforter that are more significant than words. Even when words are spoken in good faith, often they will become secondary to the supportive physical and non verbal presence of another human being. How many times do we hear someone say, 'It's hard to describe how I feel?' Even when using words and verbalising experiences is possible, we might not always comprehend the exact feeling being experienced. Being able to communicate and have our feelings understood is so important whether they be happy, sad, anxious, or in pain, to name but a few. Our aim as music therapists is to be aware of and acknowledge the range of emotional feelings, using music to be alongside the children and young people and their parents.

Creative processes

Sometimes it may be hard to imagine not only feeling shy, but also less able than many of us to be able to make your voice heard, or your movements strong enough to create significant sounds. Part of our role is to encourage and facilitate the creative opportunities that can lead to a greater involvement and increase in self confidence.

Whether it be the practical and appropriate positioning of a microphone or amplifier, facilitating creative compositions and editing using computer music software, or using devices that pick up tiny movements and convert these into musical sounds, to offer and facilitate such media is an essential part of our role.

- Using someone's breathing pattern – the tempo of their life – as a basis for a matching musical rhythm or beat
- Facilitating teenagers to feel more freedom to express, and consequently realise greater achievement
- Special moments – tiny movements of fingers over a device creating big musical sounds and witnessing the emotional reactions that these evoke
- Supporting parents and children in creative moments together

Sometimes it is easy to get lost in the preconditions, expectations and routine procedures that accompany a particular illness or condition. Creative time, as well as being expressive, allows people to identify with the healthy part of an individual. It also provides opportunities for children on their own, or together with parents and siblings, to explore and have fun in a medium that does not necessarily need to include explanation or verbal comment, and in an environment that is often difficult to find outside the musical space. How do you communicate such experiences through words; indeed to do so might somehow be an injustice.

Best job in the world?
It would be difficult to disagree.

Val Kennedy

In my early days at Martin House I was unsure of many things- particularly how to judge a child's response to my flute playing, piano playing, singing and conversation! One day I had 'pulled out all the stops' as it were, with no response from Naomi. I decided she had probably been very bored and I prepared to end our session with one last melody on flute. To my amazement Naomi suddenly smiled, and smiled again, and then gave a sort of belly laugh. I laughed with her and the session ended with great happiness and joy. My music had touched her after all. Her response had touched my soul!

Martin House Song

Caroline Illingworth together with Christian Bedford, Callum Borders, Lucy Hosany, Olivia Lindley

This is a song that we all had such fun writing and singing together. We hope you enjoy it as much as we do.

In Boston Spa there's a special place
and I don't think its near the ocean.
I love this house. It's a very big house
And its got lots of smelly lotion.
I play in the garden all day long
I love to sing my special song.
With a little bit of this and a little bit of that
So what do you think about that?

Chorus:
Its Martin House
Its been deloused
We love it so
Don't you know?

There's a big light room that's lots of fun
with lights that shine just like the sun
And into the playroom you can come
To play with games on the PlayStation
In the music room you can sing all day
In the art room you can model with clay.
With a little bit of this and a little bit of that
Now what do you think about that?

when a child dies

All nations, tribes, religions, and even age groups have rites surrounding death. In my childhood we were always kept away from it. Funerals in the street meant closing the curtains, and if you saw a hearse with a coffin in it you held your collar until you saw a four legged animal. But times they are a changing. Death and dying and funerals are taking on different characteristics and perhaps even expectations.

The funerals I have attended as a representative of Martin House and the ones I have listened to my colleagues describing are worlds apart from my childhood. No two are the same – and that is only right. We have been invited to attend Christian based funerals that have been traditional and others that have been very special but unconventional. What follows is a fictional example from the Christian tradition, but we have also been welcomed at funerals of families from different faiths and those of no religion.

farewell sam

Sam's death, long anticipated – but still a shock – occurred last week. Mum (Sue), dad (Tony), and sister (Debs) were with him. He was fifteen years and ten months old and on the threshold of taking his GCSE's. He died in Martin House on Thursday evening and later that night was taken down to "The Little Room" where he would stay until his funeral the following week.

Family and friends came to say their farewells over the next few days. They were a varied group; those regularly and intimately involved with Sam, two brave mates from school with no experience of death who stood tentatively at the foot of Sam's bed, an aunt and uncle from the next street who shared his cares over the last three years and who shake their heads in disbelief; a "guilty feeling" aunt and uncle who postponed a visit up from Hampshire last month and who now can only bring armfuls of flowers and grandma, who will forever struggle that her only grandson died almost sixty years younger than her. Over the next few days they come to Martin House and take the unique journey down the main corridor to farewell Sam. There are health professionals, family friends, the local vicar, the head teacher, the lady from the corner shop and the lady from the Muscular Dystrophy Support Group.

Sue and Tony almost ache from hugs often finding themselves as comforters rather than comforted. The paper tissue boxes are quickly depleted.

For Sam's immediate family, the pain comes in waves. For dad it is the final realisation of lost dreams of the match, and going to Speedway and fishing; for sister Debs a feeling of abandonment that the normal brother/sister scraps are over..... for ever. And for Sue, the indescribable loss of her special baby. Since diagnosis some 11 years ago she knew this day would come. Initially she tries with little success to cling to the comfort that he is free now, not only of the pain, but all the paraphernalia that leeched itself to his illness – the wheelchair, the hoist, the ventilator, his toilet chair, the suction machine...an endless list.

For a while the sitting room next to the Little Room is the family's base for receiving this stream of visitors. It becomes an obstacle course of tea-mugs, flowers, tissue boxes, sympathy cards, biscuits, photos...and pads of A4 paper. For over the next few days this room becomes an operational centre as Sue begins to activate the plan she has held in her head for years....... no dirgey funeral for Sam, but a celebration of his life. She looks for anagrams of funeral and can only come up with real fun........too corny for Sam and so she digs for something deeper.....

The day of sam's funeral

It is a bleak February afternoon. The grave yard is dotted with lingering remnants of last week's snow. The mourners are gathering in little huddles. All have complied with Sue and Tony's wish for no black and lots of red and white – United's colours. So there are red ties and jackets, shoes, handbags, single red roses, and a 'kop-ful' of red and white scarves. As the hearse arrives, the irreverent smokers stub out their cigarettes on ancient gravestones and join the main crowd by the church door.

The dark solemn funeral director, top hat and tails – but with the almost amusing concession of a red bow tie – lets the family out of the limousine and supervises the coffin's short trip to the church door. The family follow dressed as bright as Coldstream Guards; Mum and Debs in bright red trouser suits, Dad in a United track-suit. But before the coffin is brought in Sue stops the whole proceedings, "Hang on, Jim," she announces to the assembly, "You lot go in first and no hogging the back pews or there's no bun fight after!" There is a ripple of laughter as Sue's joke hits its mark... but the tear-stained mascara exposes her struggle.

The church is packed and rises as the cortege enters to the strain of Gerry and the Pacemakers football hymn "You'll Never Walk Alone", and for those few unacquainted with this "anthem" the words appear on two screens by the altar. The coffin is settled and the vicar greets the flock of fans, "welcoming all to this lovely church of St Barnabas"…and acknowledging (after some persuasion) that he will have a minor part in this funeral which will,"…..if you all join in the spirit of the occasion, be a celebration of Sam's short but special life". He twitches nervously at the football scarf around his robes and says simply, "The family will take this service…. and that is with my blessing…..but I will make a blessing at the end of our service….er celebration….over to you, Sue."

There is a pause and with three deep breaths Sue leads her husband and daughter in front of Sam's coffin.

The pregnant pause lingers, but Sue quickly composes herself; she will not fail Sam now. She nods to Sam's young friend operating a lap-top and two recent portrait pictures of Sam light up each screen with dates beneath, stating his birth and death days.

She welcomes everyone from far and near, the old, the young, old friends, new friends and those who for practical, emotional, and even financial reasons have struggled to come. Her hand trembles, whilst the other fumbles to find and grip Tony's standing beside her. "I want to thank the Red and White Army for giving us such a sea of colour and to farewell one of their greatest fans." There is a little flutter of waving scarves near the back which gives her confidence to go on; soon she is in her stride as the images of Sam's life flash on the screen and she takes the congregation through Sam's life. Sam in his birthday suit as a baby on Scarborough beach: Sam in his pedal car: on Father Christmas' knee: Sam with the dog: with granddad: in his first electric wheelchair: in the school play (in his wheelchair): meeting the cast of Emmerdale: Sam talking to Mickey Mouse in Disneyland in Florida: canoeing in Keilder: racing his chair in a sponsored race for Guide Dogs for the Blind: meeting United before last years semi-final. The pictures are interspersed with stories and anecdotes from Sue and all serve to remind that Sam was a cheeky, big hearted, generous, bright, fun loving lad who loved life and who was so very very normal.

"That was my boy", she concludes and gently lays her rose on the coffin.

Dad stands. At first his voice is weak, almost inaudible, but Sue and Debs close ranks beside him. He coughs and starts again. His pictures are all just of him and Sam and his theme, that although he wishes things were different, he would change nothing. Sam was what Sam was. He was not a muscular dystrophy boy but a boy who had muscular dystrophy. As a son he was everything a dad could wish for. And the hugs they shared when United scored was the same bond when they hugged each evening in the last two weeks of his life. Teasing Sue with men's talk, or chatting about cars, or cheating at Scrabble or "the mucky Fathers Day card I got last year" were what this dad and lad were all about. The final few words begin to break and are lost in sobs as he places his rose on the coffin.

For Debs to follow this is hard. She waits a few seconds carefully holding the type written sheet of the poem she's written. Her voice is steady and clear. Staring ahead she is not reading from the sheet at all and slowly lowers it to her side and the words written and rehearsed flow from the heart. She places two white roses on the coffin. The roses of love and peace after a very normal love/hate relationship between brother and sister. The congregation burst into spontaneous applause for the family.... and the vicar joins in.

Any other anecdotes would seem superfluous, but there is one more statement to be made. It comes from Sam himself.

Mrs Heathersage from the English Department at Beckside Comprehensive walks to the front. 'Just before October's half-term break, we filled the last 20 minutes of a lesson with, "Famous Last Words", many of which are written in the annals of humorous history. A week after the break Sam expertly steered his chair into my office and handed me an envelope. 'Miss, that was the best English lesson we've ever had, but it made me think and it made me want to write this. Its not very good – in fact its crap – but I want you to keep it and read it one day....but not yet...you'll know when.' And I took the envelope and he whizzed off down the corridor to his maths lesson. "You're right, Sam, its not a great poem in literature terms, but it is the most beautiful poem I've ever read....." She smiles at the family who know what's coming.....

Sam's Not-so-famous Last Words

My life's shorter than it should
I've known that for years
But mines been good and full of laughs
More fun, more smiles than tears

I got a really special mum
Who shares with me great fun
I've got a real brill dad
And I'm his super son

You might think fun is missing
From a boy stuck in a chair
But I've done things you haven't done
In life I've travelled far

And mum and dad have been there
In all these things I do
My mates say they're super
I promise you that's true

I've flown, I've sung. I've scored the goals
That life has passed to me
And given back the things I could
Cus love you know is free

So when you go to heaven
And join me up above
Just leave my bloody wheelchair
And just bring me your love.

The congregation sit stunned in a silence broken by sobs. The vicar stands and ponders a few seconds. "Friends, at this point I should say a whole catalogue of prayers, but this afternoon we have heard nothing else but a prayer for Sam and finally a prayer from Sam. We commend him to God's love and care and bless him on his journey. We leave as we entered, to the football anthem." The roses carefully balanced do not shift as the coffin is raised and borne down the aisle. This time the scarves are raised and waved as the music and words swell in St Barnabas's.

By the graveside still comically stands the funeral director in his red bow-tie holding fifteen red and white helium filled balloons in one hand and a little box of earth in the other. The finalities are almost complete. The coffin is lowered; a shower of roses tumble down into the grave. The box of earth is not needed.

Sue busies herself giving out balloons to close family who have written farewells on the labels.

She gives a three-two-one countdown. "Farewell Sam, Journey well!" The balloons float, hover, then lift and dance into the grey sky, higher higher over the town, over United's ground and the far far distant hills beyond.

© Sarah Aspinall

Section Four:
Developments

© Bindy Pease

Since the beginning Martin House has been eager to learn from the children and families and to continually develop what it offers to meet changing needs and circumstances.

Working within the community and bereavement care are two examples of responding to families needs. Children and families value the flexibility of practical help and support in their own homes alongside the option of stays at Martin House. Although, as we have seen in Section One, this has been part of what has been offered from the beginning, it has grown considerably since those early days. There is now a dedicated team that provides a range of support in the community; this is described by Sheila O'Leary in Chapter Twelve together with contributions from members of the community team.

So many things around a family change when a child dies. Grief is not time-limited. The team at Martin House have always known that an important part of what they do is to be available to the family in the days, months and years after their child's death. More recently a team of visitors has been established who have specific time allocated to be alongside parents who have been bereaved. In Chapter Thirteen Linda Hedley talks about the work of the bereavement team.

Whilst Martin House has always addressed seriously ill children in the context of their families, with the benefit of close observation and increased experience we have become more aware of the challenges faced by brothers and sisters. For many years Hazel Clough has had a particular concern for the siblings at Martin House and in Chapter Fourteen she describes the different provisions in place for the brothers and sisters. Examples of the activities of some of the sibling groups are provided by members of the team who work so enthusiastically with these children.

With the benefit of medical and technological advances some children with life-threatening conditions are living longer than was previously thought possible. This meant that there was a need for hospice provision to continue longer and be available for teenagers and young adults. Hazel Clough writes about how Martin House met this challenge in Chapter Fifteen. She describes Whitby Lodge, the teenage and young adult part of Martin House, and the part for which she has had particular responsibility since it opened in 2002.

Ongoing education and training has always been highly valued at Martin House, but with the increasing complexity of some children's care such training has become ever more important. In Chapter Sixteen Linda Foley explores the vital place of education and training in Martin House and looks at some of the innovative and collaborative ways of approaching staff development and training.

The Community Team

When Martin house first began it felt strongly that the families who chose to use the hospice should be central in the provision of care. The philosophy that shaped the care provided derived from the belief that families should be listened to, respected and valued. No two families have exactly the same needs, therefore there needs to be choice and flexibility in the way in which families receive care and support.

From the beginning Martin house offered support to families within their own homes. Initially this tended to be ad-hoc and usually in response to a crisis or to enable a child to be at home during the terminal phase of their illness. No organisation remains static and as Martin House grew and developed, the number of families being supported increased, despite the reduction of our original catchment area. The provision of a structured community service was discussed.

As a member of the care team I had always felt that the families would benefit from a structured community team and that it would complement and extend the choices available to the families. I was privileged to be asked to carry out a research study looking at the feasibility of establishing a structured community team. Initially I wanted to establish what care and support was available in the region, and whether families were aware of the existing services, and if so whether they were accessing them. Following discussions and visits to established services and support options across the region it became clear that the community provision and respite services were often not suitable or available for children with life limiting illnesses. As well as the findings from my work, at the same time the need for a structured community team was also highlighted by an external research project.

Presenting my findings to the Trustees

The morning of my presentation came and I nervously presented my findings to the Trustees. As I left the room I hoped that my evidence would enable them to support the development of a structured community team. The trustees agreed and the community service started in 1997. At the time most of the other hospices were not offering community support and therefore we did not have the opportunity of sharing ideas.

At the time Martin House was supporting about 230 families (currently more than 300) and we therefore realised that we could not offer support to all the families known to us and therefore it helped to have aims and criteria in place.

The initial aims of the community service:

- to complement and enhance the care already provided
- to increase the availability of the care and support provided by Martin House
- to tailor the service to allow flexibility and choice
- to respond in a crisis situation when in-house care may not be appropriate
- to assess individual needs
- to coordinate and provide care outside of Martin House
- to liase with other agencies

It was felt that the community team should be an integral part of the care team and not work in isolation. The office was based off the sitting room so that the team and families were easily accessible. Initially the team was made up of two nurses working in the community three days a week. We realised that due to the geographical expanse of the region, and in order to offer the families an adequate period of time at each visit, the number of children supported on each day would be a maximum of two.

The service keeps growing

The community service has now been running for ten years and the feedback from the families has been positive. There are a range of reasons why families will receive care and support within their own homes and these categories have changed and increased over the years. Martin House, due to its independence, can react proactively and much faster than the statutory services. For some families the support may be offered over a period of time, for others it may be at a point of crisis.

One of the visits offered to all families is the initial visit. Historically, families whose child was going to be using Martin House were first asked to come for a visit. For some families the realisation and acceptance that your child has a life limiting condition is a time of loss and shattered hopes and dreams for the child's future. Some families found that coming to the hospice for an initial visit was overwhelming. Many families had no experience of a hospice and those who did had often visited an adult facility. To initially meet a family at home enables the family to tell their own story and to have a discussion about how Martin House may best meet their needs and any concerns they may have.

A flexible service

Some families feel that community support best meets their needs. Other families may need to have some community support to enable them to feel that a stay in house would be right for them. There are a group of children that need to have regular support over a period of time. For some children and young people their condition makes it difficult to attend school regularly or at all. At times the physical and mental energy required to care for a child with a life limiting condition can be exhausting. Often the parents or guardians need time to recharge and have permission to focus on themselves. Many of the children have complex care needs and family, friends and relatives can find it difficult to offer to care for the child. Parents can also find it hard to trust the care of their often totally dependent child to others. Martin House can spend the time working alongside the parents until the level of trust enables the parent to leave the care to you. It can be thought that parents cannot benefit from respite unless they handover the care of the child, but from experience both in house, and in the community the caregivers will not benefit at all if you insist they leave before they are ready, all they will do while away is worry about the child. Others, however, are waiting with their coats on ready to leave as you arrive determined not to miss a moment of their time.

One of the first families we visited was a family who had a teenage son who was totally dependent, he was their only son and they had been his only caregivers. They had been offered other services in home and out but they had not accepted any of them. Mum's english was limited and my punjabi even less. They had had their son late in life and both had health concerns of their own. On my first visit mum initially had me sitting on the floor helping her with the ironing. We smiled frequently at each other, as she, I presume, told me her story. After about an hour I was introduced to her son, a handsome young man who spoke volumes with his saucer brown eyes. She carefully and meticulously showed me how to change his pad, I picked up that I was there to be taught and should at this point be content being the pupil. We then went back into the other room and she continued to iron. Over the next couple of weeks I was shown different aspects of his care; community elders would also pop in to see who I was. As time went on I was beginning to wonder how valuable my contribution was until one week I was handed the pad, my initiation period was over. Gradually I was allowed to undertake his cares and eventually mum began to pop out, initially for five minutes to the local shop, then this extended to the whole time I was there. I knew I had really passed the test when one day she handed me the iron.

The children are an integral part of a family and families have times where they want to celebrate an occasion. Family occasions make up the history and the timeline of a family. It may be difficult to attend with the child or care for the child while attending. At times it is also valuable for the sibling to realise that mum and or dad has made the time to be there just for them.

Support visits: Some times it is appropriate to be alongside a parent when the child is not there. It may be that one visit may be all that is required to discuss an issue, for others a series of visits may help a parent to think through an issue and discuss options and identify a way forward.

Terminal care: Choice at the time of death is vital; a right choice is the one that is right for the family. Some families may choose for their child to come to Martin House at this time, others prefer to be at home. They may choose this as they want this time to be a private and personal time with limited access by professionals, others may choose this option but want constant support. For one family it was important that their child died at home surrounded by things that were familiar to him. He had spent a considerable time in hospital hoping that the treatment would offer remission. After each hospital admission, home was their sanctuary, an environment they could control, a taste of normality and a place where they could come together again as a family. The terminal phase at home lasted for three days. During this time his parents had the opportunity to be with him as his parents, cuddling up on the double bed, telling stories, singing. The community team were there to be with the siblings. As young children they spent some time with their brother, but then wanted entertaining as children do. We also had the clinical knowledge to assess symptoms, change the syringe driver and field phone calls. When he died the family spent some ime with him, and then when they felt ready we all came to the little room in Martin House. The family stayed close by in Martin House for the next few days, so they could visit him whenever they wanted, and so they could also have help planning his funeral.

Hospital visits: For many of the families hospital visits become part of their life, some are planned but many occasions are unplanned. The demands on hospital staff are great and parents can find it difficult to spend time off the ward, especially if their child is totally dependent and has limited communication. At times it has been appropriate to spend time with a child in hospital enabling the parent to spend time out or go home to spend time with the other children. At other times parents have appreciated the time to have a coffee and a chat.

It was recognized that for some families the best community support we could offer was caring for the siblings and Hilary Clayton describes her work in this role at the end of this chapter.

Links with other agencies

Martin house does not work in isolation and links with other agencies are vital to ensure that families receive a package of care which best meets their needs. As Martin House has reviewed and changed its provision of care, community care and support across the region has improved and in many areas increased. The new opportunity funding enabled us to work collaboratively across the region. As well as the establishment of paediatric palliative care teams we were able to employ a paediatric palliative care consultant and a consultant in clinical psychology, the first in the country based within a hospice. The paediatric consultant and the community team meet regularly with established teams across the region. Our clinical links extend out to many others across the region and we utilize their experience and expertise to ensure that the care we provide is up to date and to gain knowledge in the ever changing technical care offered to many of the children and young people.

As well as our clinical links Martin House has established links with others who can enhance the quality and life experiences of the children and young people and their families and are willing to continually support us by visiting Martin House. Such links include visits from farm animals, donkeys, motor cycles and sports cars.

Working within the community team enables you to further understand the impact and put into context a child with a life limiting condition. You can see at first hand the space a child with a lot of equipment takes and the decisions parents have to take about adapting their house. Because you tend to work in isolation you can understand the juggling parents have to undertake even to make a drink.

The community support is, and will continue to be, a vital part of the support offered by Martin House. Being alongside families in their homes has definitely enhanced the professional and personal growth of those who have been part of the team. The current head of the community team, Louise O'Leary, and one of the team members, Chris Rattray who has recently been working in the rolling post on the community team, describe their experiences below. The chapter ends with some comments from families about what the community service has meant to them.

Louise O'Leary

I have worked on the care team at Martin House as a nurse since 1989. Ten years ago with Sheila I was involved in the setting up of the present community service. I very much valued the opportunity to take the Martin House philosophy into the community, working alongside families in their own homes. It is a privilege to share in a small part of the families' home lives, building up many special memories, both happy and sad.

A very important part of the community work for me has been to allow more flexibility in how families use our service. Even though most do choose to stay in the House, a small number do not. To be able to offer these families home support provides an important service in its own right and also a link; by establishing a relationship within their own homes we may be able to build their confidence in us should they decide they do want to stay at Martin House in the future. Recently, for example, we have been providing weekly home support, over several months, to a family whose child is newly diagnosed. They are aiming to come to Martin House for day care in the next holidays, when one of the community team can be available to support them and provide continuity. This may lead to an overnight stay. This process has enabled the family to establish important links in their own way and time.

Some families never go on to use the in- house service, but still maintain a strong link through community support. One such family chose to only use the community support; over a period of time we were able to establish regular respite visits, crisis support, sibling support and medical advice. In the beginning, whilst recognising their need for help, the parents were unsure about having carers in their home. However, given time and space, they came to value the care and built up a strong bond with the community team. Even though they never stayed I feel they still felt part of the Martin House family.

The flexibility of home care is central to our work. If it is more appropriate on a particular day to do the shopping or ironing than care for the sick child, this is what we will do. Though I do not think I could ask one mum for an ironing reference after burning a hole in her son's new trousers!
Support for families on special occasions is important, as this is often a time of mixed emotions. I had the privilege to care for a child during his sister's wedding. This allowed his parents to concentrate on her day, knowing their

son was still a central part of a very special family occasion. The sun shone and many happy memories were made.

During my time in community I have seen the service grow and develop. Our community hours have increased to include a yearly rolling post from within the care team, giving the opportunity for staff to work alongside families at home. A post has also been established to work specifically with siblings of children receiving community care. Liaison with local community teams has grown and regular meetings have been established. Despite its growth the Martin House community service has kept its philosophy of flexibility and family centred care, which is so central to its whole way of care and support.

Christine Rattray

In 2007 I was given the opportunity to work for two days a week for one year on the community team. I would be working with Louise, Angie and Hilary who are the current permanent members of the team. As I had always worked on the care team this was a totally new experience for me. I was nervous but also greatly looking forward to meeting our families in their home settings. My work has involved going to case review meetings, where parents and all health professionals involved in the care of the child meet together to discuss how the needs of the child are being met. I also do initial visits to families where

© Liz Varley

I go to the family home to talk about Martin House and Whitby Lodge and what we can offer. This is usually followed by the family coming here for a look around, then for a stay if they like the look of us!

The main part of my job has been home respite, where I look after a child at home for three to four hours whilst the parents go out, or catch up on their jobs in the house, or sleep. The families have welcomed me into their homes without exception and have always appreciated the time that we have given them. I have met lots of dogs, some more friendly than others, and I have spoken to extended family members who pop in for a chat. I have discussed recipes and fashion with mums, and tried to understand football and garden sheds with dads. Most of all I have enjoyed quiet times with the children, cuddles, feet and hand massages, stories and singing. Even in one case I have seen quite a lot of Star Trek episodes.

There have been times when the enormity of caring for these special children on my own has been a little alarming. However there are always parents and Martin House on the end of the phone for advice. It has been very important for me to see the families at home and the problems that have to be overcome, such as adapting homes if children have special equipment needs and wheelchairs.

I have also looked after siblings so that parents can spend time with their poorly child and go to hospital appointments. We have always known how important it is to acknowledge the needs of well siblings, and Hilary spends one to one time with them in her role as an experienced nursery nurse on the community team. I can also see how we can help liaise between the different services who support these families. We are a small part of a sometimes big team involved in the care given to families.

We have had lots of laughs about navigation-my satnav has been invaluable, and I have spent quite a lot of time discovering Bradford's one-way systems. Luckily I have not been late for a visit so far. The year has gone by very quickly and I have loved it. I have gained a more rounded experience and I appreciate why the families enjoy their stays at Martin House. I am pleased that I have been given this opportunity and I would definitely recommend it to other members of the care team.

Nursery Nurse in the community: Hilary Clayton

My part-time role as a Nursery Nurse in the community is to give time mainly to the siblings of those children who are visited by Louise, Angie and Chris, the nurses on the team. My visits vary from staying at the children's homes playing games and doing art projects, to going out to the cinema, bowling or even having a picnic in a park. It is their time and their choice, to choose what they would like to do. In the community you have to be flexible and be prepared to do anything that is required, and perhaps have a few extra ideas up your sleeve as well just in case!

I have visited seven year old Becca a few times. Becca comes to stay at Martin House from time to time with her brother and is a regular member of the Time 4 Us Club. On one of my visits on a nice sunny day I went to pick her up from home; she had asked if we could go to Harlow Carr gardens. A trip to the gardens was a lovely idea. I had packed a picnic in one bag and some arty and crafty stuff in another.

We jumped in the car and off we went. We had a lovely time. We chatted, we played, and then we had our picnic by the play area. Once we had eaten our sandwiches we decided we would make some musical shakers, so out of my other bag I pulled boxes, cardboard rolls, paper, scissors, masking tape and felt tip pens. Becca had wanted to make a musical instrument, after having seen them being made on a children's television programme. We had a fun time making them and afterwards we wandered around the gardens playing our shakers and making up songs as we went along our way.

Comments from parents

- 'The homecare has unlocked the door to what can often seem like a prison'.

- 'The care came at a crisis time for us. We were lucky that it could start immediately. I think things would have become much worse if it had not started immediately'.

- 'The care enables me to go out by myself or with friends. I can go shopping, have a cup of coffee or go for a swim, I can do them easily, things that many people take for granted'.

'The emergency help was vital at a time when we felt we could no longer cope looking after our child 24 hours a day. We had coped for eleven years and the prospect of no future help was too much to contemplate .Martin House stepped in to ensure we did not go under'.

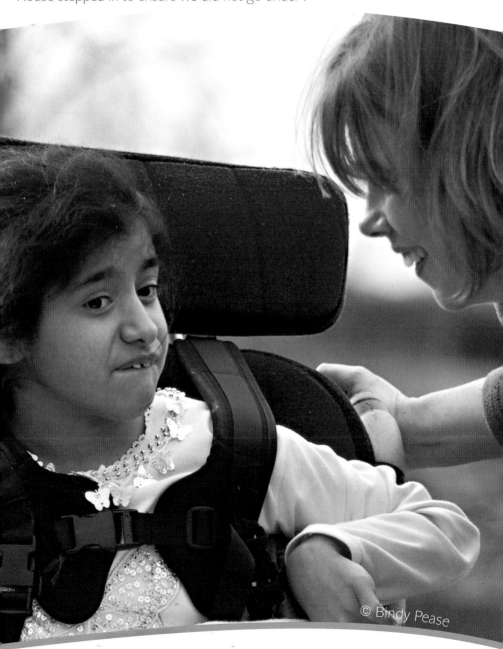

© Bindy Pease

144

Bereavement

"It is one thing to face adversity by yourself; it's quite another when you have someone in your corner. There is something amazingly powerful in supportive friends, family, words and deeds."

Bowman, Ted, (2001) Finding Hope When Dreams Have Shattered. St. Paul: self-published. Contact author at bowma008@umn.edu

Supporting families in loss and bereavement

Every family referred to Martin House is unique, but each one has many things in common. The obvious and most devastating is that they have a child with an illness or condition which is considered to be life limiting. From the time of conception it is natural for parents to look ahead, make plans and have dreams for their children. To have those dreams shattered by a diagnosis of a life shortening illness is unimaginable to most of us. The loss of those dreams is the first of many losses that our families face on the journey of their child's life. The child's condition deteriorates and each new loss brings its own challenges and need to revise hopes and dreams for the future.

An integral and hugely important part of the work at Martin House is supporting the children, young people and their families as they face these losses. We are aware that there are no quick fix solutions and we have little in the way of answers, but we try to offer steadfastness and empathy during difficult and challenging times. Every member of the Martin House staff feels immensely privileged to share in, not only some of these difficult times, but also times of joy and laughter. It is often hard for people to appreciate that a children's hospice can be anything but a sad place. The children, young people and their families ensure that it is also a place full of life and love and hope.

Our aim as a team is to be alongside families during their child's life and also to support them following their child's death. Our aim is to ensure that families are given choice about where they want to be at this most difficult time. Some families will choose to be at home with their child, whist others may use a chapel of rest in their own community. Many families choose to use the 'Little Room' in either Martin House or Whitby Lodge. The Little Room is a private, quiet, cold bedroom where a child can stay following their death and the child and their family are continued to be looked after by the care team.

Bereavement Visitors

From the very beginning, keeping in contact by telephone with families has been very important. This contact becomes increasingly important when the child or young person is ill or when difficult decisions have to be made. It is from this concept of maintaining contact with families that the bereavement team was born. Below is a letter from the two first bereavement visitors, Jo Ansty and Janet Kendall, who describe how this work first started.

Dear Linda

Thank you for asking us to share our thoughts of the early days of bereavement visiting. In the first months, we were very much learning as we went along. We were all very new to the needs of the children and families who were actively using Martin House and hadn't really thought too much about what families would do without us once their child had died. In those early days different members of the Care Team looked after the bereaved families but as the work load increased this became more difficult. We talked at staff meetings about the issue, as did the Trustees at their meetings, trying to come up with a solution. We were coming to realise what a huge impact losing regular contact with Martin House would be for some families.

At about the same time I, Janet, had the privilege of supporting a dying child in their own home and it had a profound effect on me. I kept in touch with the family by phone and then arranged to call round one evening to visit them, little realising what the outcome of that visit would be. The dad was feeling quite low and expressed feelings of anger about his child's death, but also about Martin house and the lack of contact and support they had got from us. What others might have interpreted as not wanting to intrude on grief he had seen as no one caring anymore. He felt that I was only keeping in touch because I had been there at their child's death, and that I would soon lose interest too. He said, " Is it too much to ask for someone to come and visit us once a month or something to see if we are alright?" My immediate thought was,

"No it shouldn't be!" When the mum suggested that he wouldn't talk about his feelings even if someone did come, he replied, "So what! They could still come."

With the family's agreement I relayed this conversation to Lenore, who took the issue to the Trustees. The outcome of these discussions was that Martin house would offer bereavement support to families, and we were invited to take on the responsibility for the bereaved families.

When explaining our role to families we always stressed that we were not there as counsellors (although we had both attended various courses), but as a visitor; someone to be with them and listen. We discovered that people's needs varied widely; some wanting regular phone calls, others home visits, or a chat over coffee or simply a walk together. We left it to the individual family to decide who would be present at the visit and what they talked about. We never knew what we would be confronted with on our visits; it could be taking on firework lighting duty for a mum who was terrified of fireworks, to having a rottweiler sitting on your lap – the comment "don't worry, he's just being friendly" is of little comfort!

One major difficulty was the distances that we travelled, as Martin House at that time took children from the whole of the North of England as well as Wales and Scotland. This was before the invention of the SatNav and we were reliant on what could be very dodgy directions, coupled with some equally dodgy map reading. The work could be very stressful but luckily we were both on a similar wavelength in terms of what we wanted to achieve with the work, and we both had a sense of humour. The work could be quite isolating at times but we met regularly to offer mutual support.

I hope that this history of the beginning of bereavement support is useful, and we are both sure that you know that it was such a privilege to do this work and that we wouldn't have missed it for the world.

Lots of love
Janet and Jo

Bereavement visitors usually work two days a week on the bereavement team and the rest of their working week is on the care team. It is a rotational role, on average for four years. The Bereavement team are not trained counsellors and the service they offer is not bereavement counselling. It is instead seen as an opportunity, as one bereaved parent told me, to tell and retell their stories about the life and death of their child, to someone who will listen and hear what they say without judging them. It can sometimes be easier to talk to someone who is not emotionally tied to the family rather than to a close family member or friend. Parents often comment that when they speak to their Martin House visitor they do not need to edit what they say, as they can sometimes feel the need to do in order to protect close family or friends. A couple may use the bereavement visitor as a conduit, i.e. they say something to the visitor which they may struggle to say directly to their partner.

Living with grief

In our society grief is often seen as something which needs to be over and done with as quickly as possible. The reality is that you do not get over the death of your child, but it is hoped that you will find a way of living a meaningful life alongside your grief.

This is not achieved in a few weeks or months. The role of the bereavement visitor is to work alongside the family and normalise their feelings – there is no magical formula which will make things better. Grief is painful and truly awful but it is a real and valid emotion which deserves time and recognition. The bereavement visitor not only offers emotional support to the parents but also can help with practical matters, such as contacting agencies to retrieve medical equipment, arranging a meeting with hospital doctors to talk about the time leading up to their child's death or accompanying the parents on a visit to the cemetery. One parent found it impossible to visit their child's grave but one day asked the bereavement visitor to go with her and they spent over an hour sitting at the graveside sharing memories.

Other ways Martin House offers bereavement support

Ongoing support to families is also offered in other ways. Every year we hold a special day for remembering at Martin House, to which we invite the families who have been recently bereaved.

We also run support groups for bereaved parents and for the bereaved brothers and sisters. The parents who choose to come to the groups find that talking and sharing with other bereaved parents in a safe and relaxed environment can be of enormous benefit. A parent, when asked about the support groups, wrote, "The group provides a safe, compassionate and supportive environment for parents to face and acknowledge their grief and loss, to take off the mask they wear every day to protect themselves."

We recognise the death of a child clearly affects the extended family, so we also offer support to grandparents, inviting them to a special day at Martin House so they too can share their stories and receive mutual support.

We make a commitment to all the families who come to Martin House that we will stay alongside them until a time comes when they feel able to 'go it alone'. A new member of the bereavement team recently told me, "Having worked at Martin House for six years I have always been aware of how valuable families find the support, but now that I have begun to work on the bereavement team I realise just how important it is to the families to know that there is always someone available to them. Although my experience has been relatively short, I can already appreciate that the role carries with it a huge responsibility, but that it is also a huge privilege."

There will obviously be a time when we say goodbye to every family, but Martin House as an organisation will always be here should they need it.

The chapter ends with moving words from some of the families themselves.

Michael Clements

My son

He lies so still and looks so peaceful
It is I that now feel pain
His pain is over
Mine is just beginning
I whisper his name
Knowing he cant reply
I reach out and touch him
Knowing he cannot respond

I try to convince myself
All is well
I say its best for him
He is in a better place

But tears keep falling
And I am in pieces
But time heals
And I can remember the good times
But I will never forget

coping with bereavement- a choice between existing and living: Judith Isyankova

When your child dies your heart breaks and something dies inside you as well. The world as you knew it has fallen apart, your dreams and hopes are shattered, and life is never ever the same. You might have thought that the actual death is the worst - but it is not.

No one can prepare you for the aftermath of your child's death; first the numbness, slowly replaced by the ever growing pain and despair once you begin to realise the full meaning of eternity. Then the longing for your child, the silent screaming, nobody seems to hear. You do not recognise your partner anymore, and where are those friends and relatives who were so supportive and compassionate at first? Don't people see that you are not, 'getting over it' and that it is not, 'for the best'? How do you cope with the first birthday, first Christmas, first anniversary - how can you survive when your child is dead? Why would you want to survive? To whom do you turn when grief seems to overwhelm you?

The bereavement support offered by Martin House is vital at a time when everything has fallen apart and life itself seems a huge burden. Meeting other parents in a similar situation eases the feeling of loneliness and enables the sharing of emotions, experiences and precious memories which often cannot be shared with partners, family or friends. Group discussions and activities facilitate a better understanding of the often conflicting emotions experienced during grieving, and provide coping strategies for difficult situations. The group provides a safe, compassionate and supportive environment for parents to face and acknowledge their grief and loss, to take off the masks they wear every day to protect themselves. Martin House lights up a candle of hope in complete darkness, empowering parents to learn to live with grief, making a long term choice between existing and living.

Justin and Stacey Sinclair

To all the staff

We just wanted to say a heartfelt and huge thank you to everyone who has helped us through the past eighteen months. You will never know how grateful we are for the millions of happy memories you helped to create for us, let alone the excellent care you gave to both Grace and ourselves during our numerous stays.

We would like to thank you for allowing us to use the little room with Grace last week. Because of your understanding and care we have been able to let Grace go in our own time and own way, without feeling rushed or alone.

We will never be able to explain or thank you all enough for the difference you made to our family. Thanks to you we were able to fill Grace's short life with love, laughter and fun – three things that no amount of money could buy, yet the most important things in a child's life.

Keep up the fantastic work – you cant possibly imagine how invaluable you are to families such as ourselves – and once again, thank you from the bottom of our hearts.

Yours sincerely

Justin and Stacey Sinclair
and Grace Madison Sinclair – always in our thoughts

The Hard Bits: Kathy Lawrie

It is possible to survive the death of your child. There were many days when I didn't believe it. But then there was Christine, my bereavement visitor from Martin House. 'Tell me,' I'd say, 'about the other families.' And she'd talk of parents who'd been where I was now, of how they'd not just survived, but were living life. And somewhere in that glass bubble of raw and early grief, I could begin to believe in the possibility.

Christine never denied me my grief or how bad it really was, never tried to play it down or buck me up. She was simply there, which can be the hardest place to be. And five years later, on the phone in the early hours, she was still there.

Martin House has a lot to teach the world about illness and death and bereavement. It is quite opposite to the so-called 'wisdom of the world' which would hide these things away and pretend they're not happening, so that the fiction of 'getting on with life' can be maintained. It is because my own grief was acknowledged as reality that, in time, I was able to move on, to learn to live with it (and none of that nonsense about 'getting over it').

When I arrived at Martin House my son, Stuart, had just been diagnosed with a devastating, progressive condition which would result in his death in childhood. No-one said, 'It isn't all that bad.' They said 'Yes, it's terrible,' and they gave me permission to howl, to voice my fears, to ask unanswerable questions - and they stayed there while I did it.

And here is the thing: their acknowledgement of the reality of the hard bits released me into discovering a quality of life I would not otherwise have known.

It is why I remember Martin House, first and foremost, as a place full of life –of celebration and suffering, of laughter and tears. It is why I have treasured memories of being with Stuart in his dying and after his death. No pretence, no denial. Just real life in all its fullness, and always somebody there to live it with you.

"You have your own special way
of turning the world so it's facing the way that I'm going." (Mike Rutherford, Genesis)

Thank you.

Brothers and Sisters

The importance of brothers and sisters

Brothers and sisters have always been as important to us as the parents, or even the poorly children themselves. We have over the years learned so much from the families who have been involved with Martin House, and have been able to help others through that learned experience. Giving parents the opportunity for a complete break, a chance for some time together, time to talk to each other, time to sleep, has been high on our list of priorities. It has always felt to be an essential part of the "rest and refreshment" that we have offered.

Alongside this we have tried to help families to understand how important it is for brothers and sisters to know that their mums and dads care for them just as much as they care for their poorly sibling. Sometimes we have taken on the care of the well siblings during a stay with us, so that the parents can spend some uninterrupted time with their ill child, returning home with renewed energy and patience for their other children. For other families, the chance to have their ill child cared for by a qualified team has meant that they could pack in lots of fun activities which they had not been able to do with their other children. Our experience has shown that a balance of the two seems to work well.

Starting to think about more formal support

Although we have always considered the wellbeing of the siblings and wanted to develop something which was just for them in their own right, it was a few years before we began anything formally. We were involved with literally hundreds of children, and it was difficult to know where to start. We were told by one family after their child had died, that the end of stays at Martin House since their brother had died had been a real loss and sadness to the other children in the family. They had always enjoyed their stays so much and had never realised that their brother was in fact their "ticket" to stay. They thought that we were there for them to come and have fun, and what a great place Martin House was because we could take their poorly brother too.

Groups for the siblings who have been bereaved

In 1994, after much heart-searching, training and support, we began to offer support to the bereaved siblings. Initially this took the form of weekly after school groups – offered to those children within easy travelling distance and an overnight camp, which was available for children who lived further away. Feedback from the children and families showed that both programmes had advantages and disadvantages, so gradually over the years we have developed the bereavement groups to our present format. The groups are offered to all children who have been bereaved for six months or more and are a mix of Saturday sessions and a weekend stay on a nearby farm. (These groups are described in more detail at the end of this chapter by Judy Blair.) Some children choose not to attend the groups preferring the support and help of family and friends. Our older young people, young adults in some cases, are also offered support and we try to be flexible in what is available to them.

Our message simply is that we want the children to know that we are there for them, and not just for their parents. We have seen how children "dip in and out" of sadness, they can play happily one minute yet be full of tears or very quiet and withdrawn the next. Their reactions can so often be misinterpreted by those close to them, who in the midst of their own grief may feel that they are not affected so deeply by the death of their sibling, or conversely that they are worryingly quiet and need help. It is a parent's instinctive reaction to "fix" things for their children, to make things better, to take away the pain. Children often hide their fears and sadness in an effort to protect their family, or may display other reactions if they feel it is expected of them. Through attending the groups and meeting other children in a similar situation we can help them to see that there is no right or wrong way to feel. We can also help them to discover resources for times in the future when they might particularly miss their brother or sister.

A new group

The groups for bereaved children start each year in November, and so for some children the months in between can feel like a very long time indeed to wait. For this reason, we now offer some special days at Martin House, where those children who have been recently bereaved can meet with others in a similar position to themselves and have time to relax together. They enjoy a variety of fun activities, including often preparing their own lunch together (barbecues, pizza and homemade naan bread and biscuits are particularly popular). The children recently decided to call their group The Smartinies.

Groups for Siblings of children who come to Martin House

Having successfully run the groups for a number of years for the siblings who have been bereaved, we wanted to extend the activities to those children whose siblings still use Martin House, but we were unsure of how best to start. We got just the catalyst we needed one day when Sammy made an appointment to see our Head of Care. One of her Martin House friends had been attending the bereavement groups since her sister had died and Sammy wanted to know why we hadn't thought of similar days for siblings like her whose brother still used Martin House. Quite right too Sammy! We were unsure about some of the practicalities of running days like this as we knew that for some families transporting their well children to Martin House would also mean having to bring their ill child with them, but the days would be organised just for the well ones. This has always felt an important message to give to these children – that they are just as loved and important as their poorly brothers and sisters. When families are able to make that effort for their children it reinforces this message to them.

These groups were aptly named Time4Us (which proved so popular with the bereaved children's groups, that they became known as Time4Us2). We arrange three Time4Us days each year, in the spring, summer and autumn. It has been truly wonderful to see friendships and peer support systems develop over time. These days provide an opportunity for the children to be themselves without other responsibilities, to play, have fun and to realise that they are loved and special too. Hilary Clayton gives a flavour of these special Time4Us days in a section at the end of this chapter.

Looking out for very young siblings

We have often been asked about the very young children, those under 4 years old in particular. There has frequently been an assumption that they may be too young to know what is happening, to understand or to grieve when their sibling has died. Of course each child is an individual and even at a very young age their experiences will be many and varied. They may well be used to staying with family and friends at different times of the day and night whilst parents attend appointments and hospital stays with their poorly child. They may be growing up knowing that their brother or sister has a special chair with wheels, has his dinner poured down a tube into his tummy, or spends a lot of time in bed seemingly asleep. Or there will be those who didn't see much of their sibling, sometimes in cases of more acute, sudden onset illness.

Our experience shows that one of the important things for the very young is to help them build a store of memories of their sibling, photos of them together if possible, perhaps a toy or stories written into a little book which tells of times spent together. This can then be a valuable way of helping them feel that they were included and were important to their brother or sister.

Still constantly learning

We are constantly learning from the families we meet at Martin House and have been amazed by the resourcefulness of both children and parents. There is no doubt that we will continue to see different ways of approaching the mountains that our families find they have to climb. Our task is to draw on that learned experience, to support, encourage and guide, and to always try to include and involve the brothers and sisters. At the very end of this chapter are some thoughtful words from one of the siblings themselves, Louise Wray.

Time4Us2: **Judy Blair**

Time4Us2 is the group for bereaved brothers and sisters whose ages can range from around four years old through the teenage years. The group gives the children opportunities to share their grief, ask questions and reduce the emotional isolation of bereavement. It also attempts to help the children to equip themselves with ways in which they can deal with their grief safely and over time at the same time as becoming independent from Martin House.

Running over a period of eight months, the group meets six times. We explore different aspects of grieving and loss through various activities such as games, crafts, drama and music. The emphasis is on having fun – this is very important as so often the children feel that they cannot show their enjoyment of life or their laughter might be misinterpreted as not caring about their lost sibling by parents and other adults.

Each of the groups has a theme and the activities reflect this. The first group allows the children to get to know each other and the team and is a gentle introduction to what will happen over the subsequent groups. The second group is about anniversaries and comes a few weeks before Christmas. Although the children come from varying ethnic and cultural backgrounds, they all have to deal with the difficulties surrounding particular anniversaries, such as their dead brother or sister's birthday and religious festivals. We give the children opportunities to discuss the range of emotions which can arise on these occasions and allow expression of these safely through activities.

During the next group we visit the theme of memories. One of the activities in which the children participate is the making of a memory jar - a beautiful colourful reminder of their own special memories of their brother or sister. The group about feelings is always one which brings up lots of surprises for the team as well as the children. The children are helped with the task of writing a play involving feelings and performing it with puppets in our puppet theatre.

In May, we take the children to a local working farm which is specially designed to cater for groups of children. The children are shown how to care for the animals on the farm. We go on walks and have a picnic. It is an exciting, lively, fun-filled time and it is amazing to see each of them grow a little taller over the course of the weekend. During the evening we have a candle ceremony in which we all remember someone close to us who has died. This is a very moving occasion, but most of the children like to participate. This May week-end is full of surprises and treats and one of these is the night walk that some take through the wood next to the farm. It is a new kind of experience for many, listening to the owl hooting or seeing the bats fly close. Afterwards we all gather for hot chocolate and marshmallows around the fire, followed by stories games and laughter. The week-end is exhausting for children and adults alike, but is a huge opportunity for growth and learning and fun, and for building up the much needed resilience for the children for the future.

The last group is always tinged with sadness, as this is when we say "Goodbye." Throughout the groups we have helped the children to be able to adapt to change and endings. We also give them a card with a special mobile number they can ring if they want to contact us or are experiencing particular difficulties in the future. We all go home with many memories of love, laughter, tears and sadness, and taking with us that special feeling of Martin House.

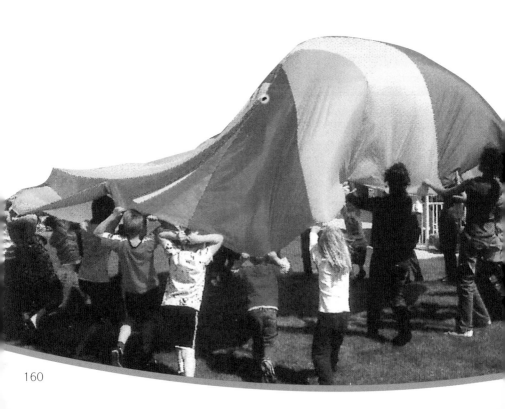

© Bindy Pease

The Time + Us Club: **Hilary Clayton**

The day before the sibling group, a last minute trip to the supermarket is required. The seminar room is prepared; bunting hanging from the ceiling, blue and white chequered tablecoths placed over the tables. We are almost ready for our Food Theme day.

The Time 4 Us team are at Martin House bright and early. Pete and Nige put up the marquees. The garden is tidied, the outdoor games are put out. Sarah and Amanda prepare the food for the ready steady cook competition. With a cup of coffee and a piece of toast in hand we discuss again our plans for the day. We are well organised.

We wait in anticipation for the children to arrive. At 10.30 twenty five children descend on the seminar room. One little girl arrives with her Time 4 Us invitation card and a little letter she has written telling us how much she was looking forward to coming to the Time 4 Us Club. The day has started. Introduction games are played, then with hands washed and aprons on, the ready steady cook competition begins. Ainsley Harriot couldn't attend, we did well without him! Pizzas and meringue desserts are made. Jan and Volunteer Kath do pizza relays to the ovens in the seminar room and Whitby Lodge to get all twenty five pizzas cooked and ready on time. Volunteer Vicki judges the competition. All the children do a wonderful job and all win a prize. Lunch has been prepared and how tasty it is too.

The weather stays fine and in the afternoon the children choose what they would like to do, from building a den, to seeing who can throw a carrot the furthest, eating donuts dangling from a string (no hands), playing football and making place mats. Vegetables are grown every year in the Time 4 Us allotment. Today gardeners Gillian and Janet plant peas and sunflower seeds with the children. We wonder whose sunflower will grow the tallest. Mary brings along her animals from her farm for the children to feed, take for a walk, stroke and play with. The goat does not come in fancy dress today.

The time has gone quickly, the day is coming to an end; a few more games are played and then at 3.30 we all say goodbye – until next time. With the children safely on their way home, Nige, Amanda, Sarah, Jan and Hilary tidy up the seminar room and garden and then sit down with a well earned lovely mug of tea and chat about the day.

What do the children say?

I don't like it here – I love it!

I feel full of joy! Time 4 us is fun.

Time 4 Us club really rules! once again

Louise Wray, 14yrs

Although hospices can be seen as negative places, Martin House is different because they are very family friendly. The staff are always welcoming, encouraging and friendly towards everyone, which really does benefit the entire family. All the family being together when having an ill brother or sister is important because living with an ill sibling can sometimes be upsetting and stressful. Hospices like Martin House are different from hospitals because they allow more freedom for your ill brother or sister and the rest of the family.

You also have to remember that, even though your sibling may be ill, positive things will come from the experience, such as making friends with similar experiences and learning lots of new things. One of the music therapists at Martin House encouraged me to be musical and today, more than 10 years later, I am still continuing with flute and am now even into composing my own music.

Never forget: Even the darkest of clouds have a silver lining.

whitby Lodge

We are very proud of Whitby Lodge, which, when it opened in 2002, was the first purpose built unit of its kind for teenagers and young people in the world. The recent advances of modern medicine have seen many children able to enjoy a better quality and longer life than those who first came though the doors of Martin House when it opened in 1987. However this meant that some of our young people began to outgrow Martin House as their needs and priorities were very different from the younger children and families who use us. We knew that we needed to consider a separate facility.

Planning stage

We began to think about Whitby Lodge by including every young person over the age of 13, checking out how they felt about whether they would like a separate facility. We then built up a picture of the kind of place that they would like to use. Some teenagers were able to be a part of the discussion groups with our architects, others sent us their own wish lists. Ideas ranged from automatic doors to outdoor party areas. Many of the suggestions were incorporated in the plans; the cheekier wishes (such as naked male cleaners and no staff over the age of 21) were carefully considered!

The planning of the teenage/young people's unit coincided with a time of change for the sisters from The Order of the Holy Paraclete who had been involved with and worked alongside us since the idea of Martin House was first conceived. They were no longer able to support as many communities with a physical presence as they had previously managed, and so their return to Whitby would leave us with an empty building in our grounds. We were able to add a purpose built bedroom wing and to adapt the existing accommodation. We also managed to incorporate many of the ideas which came from the young people themselves. The Whitby sisters were enthusiastic about the exciting new plans for their "home" and have continued to be enormously supportive of all our work. The name Whitby Lodge was chosen by one of our teenagers in acknowledgement of the sisters.

Choosing to stay in Whitby Lodge

We offered Whitby Lodge to all the children using us who were 13 or over, but there was no obligation for them to change, the choice was theirs. Some were eager to start and others took it more slowly, making a more gradual transition.

One of the most popular requests for Whitby Lodge was that parents should not routinely stay; a memorable quote from one of our young men being, "Other people's parents are alright, but it's your own that you don't want around". This was no reflection on the relationship he had with his family, but rather that he wanted to experience some "normal" independence. There is family accommodation available; for example, should a young person be very ill, or maybe if they need some parental reassurance when they first choose to try the Lodge. There is also the flexibility of Martin House being next door if extra family rooms are needed.

The proximity of Martin House has been a distinct advantage when it comes to children approaching the age that they might make their own transition into Whitby Lodge, a kind of growing up. Those children who have been used to stays in Martin House with their family will often take tentative peeps before they decide to change; others can't wait and will give plenty of warning of their approaching 13th birthday. Having flexibility has been a good model and it has been much less scary than it potentially could have been for some children.

valuing the independence

Ask our young people what it is that they like about Whitby Lodge and they will tell you many things; being able to move about the house without having to ask for doors to be opened, being able to choose what to do, where to go on trips out, what and when to eat, when to go to bed. Ismail feels he is well looked after and enjoys the peace and quiet. Adam loves the relaxed atmosphere and the fact that there is such a wonderful large accessible garden. Dominic told us that there are still not enough young female care team! Many also value being able to experience some measure of independence from their families.

It has been wonderful to see how much support the young people give to each other. Several of them have reached college or university, an achievement in itself. However, arranging suitable accommodation and engaging care staff can be a veritable minefield, and so learning from the experience of their Whitby Lodge "mates" has been incredibly helpful to many.

popular activities

We had assumed that computers, films and music would figure largely in the choices that they make during their stays. We had not bargained for the popularity of board games; Scrabble, Uno and other similar games. There is much laughter around the table, often late into the night. Nor had we quite appreciated that the planning together of exciting meals and having long and lively after dinner discussions, would give so much pleasure. One young man who loves fine food yet sadly cannot manage to eat very much of it, still enjoys choosing and supervising the cooking of gourmet food.

care towards the end of life

It feels very important to enable the young people to have as much choice as they can and this is particularly true when it comes to care towards the end of life. The nature of progressive illness means that many of the things which happen to them will have been out of their control, that they have little or no choice at some stages of their illness. Whilst some of our young people have wished to stay at home with their families for care at the end of their life, others have chosen to be at Whitby Lodge. There have been times when our small building has felt quite full of family and visiting relations and friends. We then try hard both to give the family the privacy they need, and to make sure that any other young people staying during that time also enjoy their stay and feel comfortable. One lovely chap told us that he had been impressed by the care given to the parents and siblings, and that it had greatly reassured him that, "when it comes to the time for me to die, I know now that you will look after my family."

The future

Looking at all the changes which we have seen over the last 21 years brings us inevitably to think of the years ahead. How will Whitby Lodge be working in the future? Some of the young people who use us are starting to explore the idea of living 'independently' away from the family home and with their own identified carers. We had wondered whether that would mean that stays in Whitby Lodge no longer had the same appeal for them, as they no longer needed that change from home. However, our experience so far is that these young people still value Whitby Lodge enormously. It provides continuity, which is much appreciated in difficult times. It also provides companionship and friendship on what can be a lonely journey. The opportunities to share with others in similar

© Bindy Pease

situations, and the friendships forged can provide powerful, supportive and healing bonds.

It is difficult for our young people to be spontaneous in their choices, something which many others perhaps take for granted. One of the young men, Greg, describes even a night out with friends as rather like arranging a military operation. A relatively simple wish such as to attend the Edinburgh Festival can turn into frustration when it becomes obvious that there is simply nowhere available which is suitable for him and a carer to stay. Perhaps in 21 years from now this will be different, but in the meantime, Whitby Lodge can help to fill some of those needs.

One thing we do know is that we will always continue to listen to the young people themselves. We will not presume to know what will work but we shall continue to learn from them and be guided by their wishes.

© Bindy Pease

Anthony McFadden

Katie, my sister, and I have been coming together since May 1988, so we know both the House and the Lodge well (better than some of the staff). As soon as the nuns left, we watched Whitby Lodge develop. When a lady came to help design it I discussed the draft plans with them all at some length. (Katie was too busy out shopping!) There were two main points that I was particularly adamant about: the first was to have a water feature in the courtyard and the second was that there should be a conservatory. At that time there wasn't one in the main house, but the conservatory in the Lodge was such a success that they had one put in later.

© Bindy Pease

A quick overview of a day in whitby Lodge:
Adam Tempest

Hi, my name is Adam Tempest. I love the way we are cared for in Whitby Lodge. My day begins at 11.00am; you may think this is late to be getting up, but I didn't go to bed until 4.00am the previous night due to having fun and watching DVD's with the night staff. After my jacuzzi bath I am fully awake and ready to start the remainder of the day. We have many trips out during our stay, but on this particular day I was being looked after especially by Nige and we walked down to the village pub. This is good as it is easily accessible in my wheelchair and I get to do what all 25 year olds enjoy, drinking and looking at the local talent. We also enjoy a one to one chat about future life issues away from the non-stop activity at Whitby Lodge. We have a laugh on the way back to the Lodge, me taking the mick out of Nige's choice of jukebox music - I've never heard of 'Golden earing'.

we never stop learning: Pam Smith:

It is 3.30pm, a young man in his twenties arrives for his respite stay. He is fully ventilated, has a tracheostomy and seems to have enough technology around him to guide a small plane into landing. I say a silent prayer that I am not left in sole care of him. His room soon resembles that of an intensive care unit. As he passes he smiles and winks at me. I feel as if he has just yanked at my heart strings.

Next morning my whole aim is to care for this young man to the best of my abilities. My team mates support me in the morning and I become his main carer in the afternoon. He patiently guides me round his technolgy and tells me I am doing well. Later that evening I ask him how he remains so patient. He says,'If you have time for people and love in your heart, that's all you need.'

Vanessa Richardson

No chef in Whitby Lodge; how would we cope without Robin's daily culinary skills? Answer: Somehow, none of us quite knows how, five of us have each done little bits to get a beautiful meal on to the table. Miracle meals we often call them. As care team members some of us have developed cooking skills we never thought we'd have, others who are more confident just seem to throw things together…and voila, a lovely meal. Some have their specialities, mine being yorkshire puddings that rise a treat.

What's been great is the teenagers trying different foods, and also creating them. One young man makes us chilli each time he comes, but he doesn't add the chilli powder as he hasn't got much of a sense of taste and would blow our heads off. Another loves cooking but is unable to do it himself. He brings his own recipes with him, usually for fish which is his passion. He directs us in what to do for the recipe and it is usually delicious. The only exception was when his auntie bought him fresh smoked cod roe as a birthday present to make taramasalata. We did it, thanks to a recipe on the internet. The end result? No-one was keen, but he had enjoyed making it and there was lots of fun in the process. Even if we don't repeat that one, I know he and others will continue to create tasty treats in the Lodge kitchen.

Amy Livesey

I started coming to Martin House when I was 15 years old. Whitby Lodge hadn't been 'born' then so my first few stays were in the House.
For my first stay I just stayed for the night but then I progressed on to staying two or three and now at the Lodge I have even longer stays so it means my parents can have a little holiday or visit my sister abroad.

I have quite varied interests and my stays at the Lodge reflect that. I have the opportunity to go out to the cinema, which I do at home too but it's not always possible so it's great to do it at the Lodge. I also go out shopping sometimes, often to places I would only ever visit if I was staying in the Lodge such as York or Leeds.

My dressings are the main factor in the management of my condition. It's the most time consuming and major part of my care and because of the nature of my condition they are always done a certain way. Obviously this made me quite nervous about visiting the House and having somebody else other than my Mum doing my dressings. Having been away once before and having a problem with how my dressings were done I was a little wary. But I was 15 and wanted to try and have a break from home. When my family and I came for a visit it felt a really homely place and definitely somewhere I wanted to stay. The care team listened really carefully about what my care involved. They admitted that although they may not know everything about my extremely rare condition, they would do everything to make sure they understood. They kept their promise and my first stay went brilliantly, so from then on they couldn't keep me away.

When the Lodge opened I was really looking forward to it. It meant that I could always mix with people my age during my stays and I would be able to relax in an environment totally catering for my age group. I thought the place looked amazing and knew I would enjoy my stays even more.

Back to my dressings, that is how my day always begins whether it's at home or the Lodge. It's the biggest part of my care so when I stay in the Lodge it's the biggest thing the care team have to deal with when it comes to me.
It usually takes two of the care team to do my dressings and the more stays

I have the more people learn how to do them. I have to have a bath to get the previous dressings off and then after that I am re-dressed. It can take a number of hours but the care team make it as painless as possible. I listen to music while I have my bath and dressings off, then often we put a film on to watch while my dressings are being put on. I'd imagine you can hear raucous laughter or sobbing coming from the room depending on what film we are watching.

When I am finished or when they are finished, it's usually time for lunch so we make our way down to the dining room where I can have whatever lunch has been prepared for everyone or something else if I want. After lunch the care team often have to go back to my room to clear up (I make a bit of a mess), so they are still working hard just as I start to relax even more. Then my day will go one of two ways, stay in or go out. If I go out I usually go to the cinema or shopping often accompanied by someone else who is staying in the Lodge.

The care team have to put up with a lot from me whether we go out to the cinema or shopping. They could be having to endure a dodgy romantic comedy or period drama, which I have a tendency of wanting to see, or they have to help me decide which colour handbag to have and which shoes to buy to go with the bag. Then, laden with bags or mopping up tears, we return to the Lodge usually in time for tea. After tea and Hollyoaks (Hollyoaks is essential), I relax in front of the TV before the night staff arrive. When they do we get drinks, sometimes ice cream milkshakes, and pick a DVD. If we're lucky and it's a girly lodge then it's usually a romantic comedy or old weepy but sometimes we let the boys reign and do an action movie. Then as I've been out I would probably have an early night, and by early I mean just before midnight .

The next day would probably be a bit more relaxing. I would get up the same way I do every morning and then have my lunch. In the afternoon I will probably watch some TV, go on the internet and check my emails, play on the playstation or I might get my laptop out and have a play on that. Then I might watch a DVD or do some art, depending on what I feel like, it's entirely up to me. I might have a bit of a late one that night and squeeze in two films before I go to bed. Then I get changed into my PJ's and buzz for the night staff to give me my meds and hook me up to my gastrostomy feed. And then I sleep ready for another day at the Lodge.

I never wake up dreading having my dressings done because although it can be sometimes painful and traumatic, the care team make it fun so all I have to worry about is what film to watch that morning.

P.S. Not me - or my car - but I do love driving.

A Trip to Keilder: Jo Keeling, Cath Knowles and Colin Rogers

what's Keilder all about then?

Martin House, together with other children's hospices, has over the last few years had an annual trip to Keilder. It's a fabulous outdoor and indoor activity centre run by the Calvert Trust in Northumberland. It offers activities such as archery, canoeing, king swing, climbing wall, table tennis, pool, hydrotherapy pool plus much more and all with hoisting facilities to enable children and adults with different abilities to participate. The scenery is spectacular with woodland and lake views all around; you could be in another country. It certainly has the 'wow' factor. This year we shared our adventure with Derian House, Francis House and Claire House. Here is a flavour of the fun packed days.

Monday

After loading the car with loads of food and treats [courtesy of Robin], baggage and equipment, and the children Sam, David and Tashka, we waved goodbye and hit the road. After stopping on the way for a delicious picnic we finally arrived at Keilder in the early afternoon, all very excited!

We were allocated a chalet at the top of the hill; it was huge with three bedrooms, an open plan kitchen, dining and lounge area plus a veranda. After unpacking and sorting, we all went to have a look round the centre and facilities and to meet everyone.

On our first evening we were joined by the three boys and care team from Derian House. We all ate a tasty shepherd's pie and veg, followed by trifle, that Robin our chef had prepared for us to bring to make the first night of catering a relaxed affair. Sam entertained with a good line in jokes and songs.

Tuesday

Start of an action packed day, so we fuelled up with cereal and croissants before heading down to the centre for 9:30. We took part in archery competitions, went swimming and spent time handling the owls and hawks at the birds of prey sanctuary. Derian House cooked a lovely tea and one of the lads from Derian House played practical jokes on everyone with his remote fart machine.

wednesday

The King Swing; what an experience we had! We were suspended in a harness and pulled up to 20-50 feet then released to swing freely. Tashka's eyes nearly popped out of her head and even though afterwards she said it was something she wouldn't do again she was emphatic that she was glad that she had done it. Sam was dazed for about 2 hours …maybe that was Jo's screaming, who was in tandem with him. Jo certainly won the competition for the loudest scream, but Colin won for the worst chaffing from the harness!

The afternoon was a less scary event but still good fun with all the children going out on the lake in a motor boat and all having a turn at the controls.

Thursday

On our last evening at Keilder all the hospices arranged a get together and we had a fantastic BBQ. Afterwards the centre put on a disco for us and Tashka, who is an early to bed girl, managed to stay up until 9pm and get a couple of dances in. Later that evening, at David's request, we had started to tell ghost stories with all the lights off but within a minute of starting to tell the story the boys wanted the lights back on and to change the subject. They went to bed at midnight. I'm not sure who was more tired by this point but there were long 'ahhhs' from both kids and staff as we got into our beds that night.

Friday

On our last morning Sam and David were keen to go down to the centre for the last time while Tashka was booked for a foot and leg massage. We got out our pinnies and feather dusters to clean the chalet and pack up the van.

On our return to Martin House Sam was snoozing in the car and looking a little tired as his dad picked him up. Tashka was really excited to see her mum and sisters and her mum was pleased at how well she looked (despite having a holiday from hair brushing for 4 days). She commented that Tash's sister gets to go on sleep overs to friends but that Tashka never has, so this was a real adventure and something that she had looked forward to.

The young people had a great time at Keilder. David was interested in everything, and asked stacks of questions. Sam and David enjoyed each other's sense of humour and they were also real gents with Tashka. Tashka kept up the female sensibility and fun in the group. It was a real pleasure getting to know the young people better and a real delight to be able to share the adventure with them. They all said that they wanted to stay there longer, but they did give it only 9 out of 10 on account of having to get up earlier than their bodies really wanted to!

It was also great getting together with the other hospices, everyone helped each other out with providing or swapping items that others had forgotten, helping out with the children and the preparation and tidying. Derian even went shopping for some midge repellant for us. There was a real camaraderie going on and it felt like we'd known each other for a long time.

so what is Keilder all about?

It's an opportunity for children and teenagers to participate in something independent of their families, something that's good fun, exciting, sometimes scary and something that they might otherwise not get the chance to experience.

"Every time we ask her anything about it she has a huge smile on her face. The trip has done wonders for her confidence and given her such a boost"

It's also a great social experience not only for the kids but for the care team as well. Tired afterwards? "Oh yes." Would we all do it again? "In a moment".

As David was telling his mum about the trip she said, "I've never heard so much happiness in David's voice before!'

To Colin, Cath and Jo,

"Thank you for taking me to Kielder Water. I had a fantastic time. I loved everything!"

Love from
Tashka X X X

Ann Douglas

My first day as a nurse coming to work in Whitby Lodge saw me sitting round the dinner table with four young adults aged between 19 and 25 years and my colleagues dressed up in ponchos and sombreros. The young people had chosen guacamole with tortilla chips and chilli con carne, washed down with tequila with salt and lime, whilst listening to Mexican music to create the right atmosphere. There were photographs taken to mark the event in our precious photograph albums, which we often flick through and reminisce. On one such viewing a fellow staff member enquired why I appeared so bemused in the photo, but understood completely when I said it was my first day.

This was my first of many unusual shifts spent in the Lodge, and of many more themed days from around the world. The idea of the themed days, picking a country to plan a day around, was originated by one of the young people expressing disappointment at not being able to visit Japan. So the staff decided to bring Japan to him. We have had belly dancers, a 'dunney' constructed on the patio, we've had 'Bond' days, 70's and 80's days, all entered into with equal enthusiasm by the staff and young people alike.

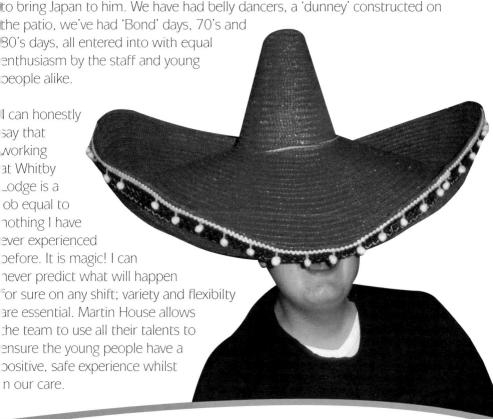

I can honestly say that working at Whitby Lodge is a job equal to nothing I have ever experienced before. It is magic! I can never predict what will happen for sure on any shift; variety and flexibilty are essential. Martin House allows the team to use all their talents to ensure the young people have a positive, safe experience whilst in our care.

AN OT'S journey: Mary Newbegin

I have worked as an occupational therapist in Leeds for over twenty years. During this time I have worked in a variety of posts, mostly in paediatrics, including work in mainstream and special schools, child psychiatry, the child development centre at St James Hospital and most recently as part of the neuromuscular team at Leeds General Infirmary. I have been lucky enough to enjoy all my jobs but I felt that I had really found my niche in my post at the LGI, and I intended to stay there for several years. However, sometimes things don't quite go as you plan.

Six years ago I attended the International Neuromuscular Conference in London. I was hoping the conference would be of benefit but little did I realise what a change it would bring about. On my return journey from King's Cross, I just happened to get onto not only the same train, but into the same carriage as three physiotherapists. These three were no ordinary physios but were Hazel, Elaine and Viv, the physios from Martin House. The journey passed quickly for me as I listened with interest to stories about Martin House. I also learned that Hazel had recently been interviewing for care team posts as the new teenage unit, Whitby Lodge, was soon to be opening. Funnily enough the next week I found myself having a look around Martin House and returning home with an application form!

A couple of months later I couldn't believe how lucky I was to be working in such a fantastic environment with such brilliant team! I also found it both refreshing and rewarding to be learning so many new and varied skills involving the total care of the young people. Like many others on the care team, I was employed as one of the team who just happened to have other skills, to be put to use when needed. However, I'd not been working in the Lodge long when one of the young people asked me, 'What, as an OT, would I be contributing to Martin House?' 'Help', I thought, ' I wasn't even asked this at my interview.' I somehow managed to waffle some inadequate answer, and he kindly let me off the hook. A few years on I hope I might be able to give a better answer.

As a student OT, I remember being taught that the philosophy of occupational therapy was all about treating the individual holistically, looking at the needs of all involved in their care and that treatment should always aim to be 'client led'. I was also taught that the skills required to make a good OT were to be flexible, adaptable, empathetic, a good communicator, to be able to problem solve and to be able to work as part of a team. Well, if over the years I've begun to develop a few of these skills, they seem to fit pretty perfectly into being part of the team at Martin House. Yet again, how lucky am I?

It takes a while to find your feet when you start work at Martin House. It feels as though you have so much to learn and that all the team know so much more. I was fortunate in some respects though, as having 'been round the block' for a number of years in Leeds I knew some of the families who used Martin House. In particular, I knew many of the young men with muscular dystrophy. This really helped me settle into my new job and I thank all of you who unknowingly helped me find something familiar to help me along the way.

Since starting at Martin House I have managed to maintain and redevelop many of my links with therapists in the community. This has often proved useful when liaising on behalf of families regarding problems with wheelchairs, equipment or adaptations amongst other things. I am also able to let students and therapists come and spend time with me. Something in some of my previous roles I would have found extremely helpful in order to gain better insight into what most families have to deal with on a daily basis. I am still as delighted to find myself working here as I was the day I started. I learn something new every day and I continue to have increasing admiration for our young people and I am frequently humbled by their actions and achievements. I am hoping that I have found my niche this time, but I still sometimes wonder what I would be doing now if I hadn't stepped onto that train!

Nudrat Afza

The photograph on the following page hangs in the Lodge at Martin House. It was originally part of a commission to photograph diverse communities in the north of England. I am so pleased to have the picture on permanent display here because the support and care that my daughter Khadijah and I have received over the years has in some ways enabled me to pursue my passion for photography. It is a privilege to reflect on the compassion and kindness of everyone involved in Martin House and to be part of what is a unique place.

Katie McFadden

This is me
the art of children

I was delighted when my painting was accepted for the 'This is me' exhibition in London, organised by Children's Hospices UK. I made it of parts of my face that I painted from photographs of me at different ages.
Christian Slater liked the eyes, especially the baby eye.

Katie with Hollywood star Christian Slater

Education

As Martin House developed and the care team expanded so did the ways we supported and developed the team at Martin House. A few years ago a post was created for someone to develop the role of education and training, which I was appointed to do. Before taking up this role I worked full time as a nurse on the care team soaking up knowledge and skills from my team-mates, the children and families as well as applying my own professional skills.

Team development

When looking at training and developing the care team there are many elements to consider, not just the clinical ones. Each of us has to be a caring person who has the necessary practical skills but also knows how to be alongside someone who is having a really tough time, be that a non verbal child, a frustrated angry teenager or a mother who emotionally is in a totally different place to her partner. How the team accrue those skills will depend on their professional background, their life experiences and personality.

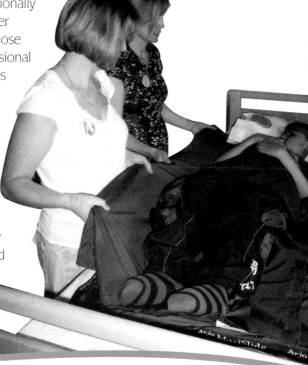

Having a mixture of experiences, professions and backgrounds helps towards developing an environment where we can learn from each other, from the children and their families and enable a family centred approach to the care and support we deliver. I have always likened our care team to a box of liquorice allsorts!

Flexible approaches to learning

Alongside this way of learning there has also been a structured approach to attaining new skills that has grown and developed over the years.

In the early days courses on children's palliative care did not exist, but we learnt palliative skills from our colleagues in adult hospices, paediatric services, social services, education and family support groups that could be transferred over to children and young people with life limited illnesses. As more children's hospices opened and expertise developed dedicated study days and support services have been established, with children's hospices communicating between themselves and collaborating in sharing and teaching new skills and good practice. Every year in-house training takes place at Martin House with statutory updates as well as relevant speakers from inside and outside Martin House giving their time and expertise. Each year I am always amazed at the expertise within the team and the enthusiastic way they share their knowledge and skills. Over the years Martin House has helped support team members with relevant courses, examples include nursing, communication, spiritual care and bereavement support

Once weekly afternoon sessions called 'Time Team' have recently been developed. These are delivered by members of the team or outside professionals. They are highly valued by the care team and cover a vast number of subjects. Carol Sykes explains about the ethos behind them at the end of this chapter.

Changing needs

In 1987 we were a smaller care team caring for the children and young people; as the number we are supporting has increased so has our team. Alongside this is the increasing complexity of care for some of the children and young people and a higher degree of knowledge and expertise needed. The balance between acquiring these new skills and still recognising the unique child or young person is a challenge that is undertaken every day. To help support and facilitate the learning of these skills within the team we now have a clinical support practitioner, Carol Sykes. Carol works alongside the team, enabling them to progress their expertise and further develop their skills. On the following page she gives an example of how the team might approach a specific clinical situation:

Planning for Sally's next stay and keeping up to date with her changing clinical needs

'Sally's mum contacted the Hospice about her next stay which was two weeks away. Sally would need some special treatment during her stay. She would need intravenous antibiotics twice a day through a 'port a cath.' (This is a simple device which is inserted under the skin and allows drugs to be given directly into the blood supply entering the heart. The drugs can be sent directly and more efficiently into all parts of the body. Blood specimens can also be taken via this route avoiding repeated needle stabs.) The antibiotics were in special devices which can be attached to the 'port a cath'.'

In preparation for Sally's visit it was recognised that the care team would need up to date training for this procedure. The clinical support practitioner nurse liaised with the family and with the nurse specialists and identified the training needs the care team would need. It was agreed with mum and Sally that a nurse from Martin House would go with them to clinic and observe the procedure in clinic. (The clinical support practitioner nurse had previous experience and knowledge of this procedure but wanted to be fully familiar with how it worked for Sally.)

The following day the clinical support practitioner nurse visited Sally's home along with the specialist nurse and observed a demonstration of the procedure using the 'port a cath', and specialist device for giving intravenous antibiotics in the community. She was then observed and supervised by the specialist nurse, carried out the procedure and was signed off as competent by the specialist nurse. Over the next few days the clinical support practitioner nurse set up simulated training sessions for the nurses at Martin House. The nurses practiced the procedure with the equipment and were observed carrying it out. The care team were happy to change shifts and were flexible in freeing up their colleagues for them to do the training. A care plan was devised in partnership with Sally and her mum. This would be implemented whilst Sally was at the Hospice.

The care team try to be proactive in their care for all the children and young people at Martin House. They are enthusiastic to learn new techniques and maintain up to date care and safe practice. The above is an example of how the team here at Martin House work in partnership with families and other specialist services. The team recognise the importance of ongoing training in providing optimal care for children and young people.

Sally's stay at Martin House Hospice was uneventful; treatments were carried out effectively and competently. The treatment did not interfere with Sally's stay or her normal routine. She still managed to have her nails painted, enjoy her frequent trips to the light room and be very creative in the art room.'

collaboration

We have not developed in a vacuum, other children's hospices have opened throughout the country, and over the years an association of children's hospices, initially started by Lenore Hill and the Head of Care at Helen House, has progressed the exchange of ideas and good practice, and the development of children's palliative care throughout Great Britain [Children's Hospices UK]. It is an exciting time in education and training as we look at innovative and collaborative ways of staff development and training, within children's services broadly and children's palliative care services in particular.

Nationally a training structure is being developed with a flexible approach that will find ways of recognising and crediting knowledge acquired in many different ways, not just a straight academic approach. Martin House has developed links with universities, colleges and educational leads, and alternate years with Bradford University we run a module here at Martin House for health care professionals. It is a two way street, not only do we offer advice, support and training, but our professional colleagues frequently do the same for us. We are always eager to learn new skills and they are generous in the amount of support they give to us.

At regular intervals during the year we hold professional afternoons where colleagues working in other areas of palliative care can come and gain insight into our work. This develops links with other services and helps make more individuals and services aware of Martin House and the work we do.

A parent's perspective on quality of care

A few years ago I was sitting listening to a mum giving a talk about what quality of care she wanted for her child. She was responding to the then new Care Standards Document, where we have to show we are attaining minimum standards. She voiced her wish, and I am sure every parent's wish, that they want the maximum, not the minimum, level of care for their children when being cared for by a children's hospice. So when we are looking at meeting standards, training and developing our team and ticking all the boxes, we keep our philosophy in the forefront of our minds and give the best level of care we can.

Years ago at a conference I heard Sister Francis Dominique [one of the founders of Helen House] give a talk about the different ways we learn how to give supportive children's palliative care, what she said will stay with me forever;

"The children and their families are the teachers, we the care team are the pupils, it is a master class".

Sue Hayes

Memories of my placement at Martin House

My first and lasting memories of Martin House began the instant I walked through the door. Every member of staff and family I came into contact with from day one made me welcome. The atmosphere of the place is apparent, it is relaxed, friendly, happy and safe. Whilst on this placement as a student paediatric nurse I learnt so very many new skills and improved some old ones. I shall take them with me and use them in my future practice. Moreover I shall take with me so many lovely memories that I will treasure forever.

Team Time: Carol Sykes

There is no " I" in TEAM

Teamwork is the essence of Martin House. 'Team Time' gives the team an opportunity to meet up for one hour a week. It is a very important hour - time to catch up, reflect and spend time together.

The hour sessions are informal, looking at a broad range of different issues; care, play, professional development, alternative therapies, innovation, technology (knowing how to switch on a play station is a must), and communication. Keeping ourselves up to date is very important.

The care team has a wealth of expertise and experience; 'Team Time' gives colleagues the opportunity to share this with each other. Some sessions are facilitated by outside speakers, experts who are more than happy to come and share their knowledge with the team. In turn the team can take their expertise to outside sources. We have built up an amazing net work of colleagues and enjoy working in partnership with them.

Section Five:

New
Perspectives

© Liz Varley

192

There is a tension for all of us between keeping things as they are and developing and changing. Martin House experiences this too. How does it keep moving forward and adapting to change without losing the best of what it has become? With ongoing medical advances some children are living longer; this means issues are arising and decisions have to be made that previously were not considered but now have to be balanced and addressed, as their conditions progress to new levels of complexity. To help address some of these challenges, as well as contribute to the ongoing work of the hospice, external funding was sought for two new posts. The bid for national money for the innovative posts of a Consultant in children's palliative medicine and a Consultant clinical psychologist were successful and in 2004 the present appointments were made. Such posts were new to a children's hospice and as such the first of their kind. This means that these posts have provided a service both within Martin House Children's Hospice and more widely within paediatric palliative care. Dr Mike Miller and Dr Jan Aldridge describe their roles in Chapters Seventeen (Medicine) and Eighteen (Clinical Psychology) respectively.

medicine

The talk was about communication and what makes a good doctor. The slide was a Victorian painting called 'The Physician' and showed a young girl, very pale, on her bed at home. Beside her sat a tired, elderly doctor, with her even though there was little he seemed to be doing. We were being told that this showed what being a good doctor was about. At the time, as a new doctor, I was cross. Why wasn't an intravenous line in place? Where were the monitors? Where is all the high technology making it a battle to save this young girl's life? With age and experience has come some wisdom and the knowledge that even in this modern age there are times that all we should do is allow the patient to make their own choices.

medical support at martin house

Martin House has always had good medical support. A doctor is needed to review medication, check for interactions and provide alternatives for symptom management. At first the local GP visited at lunch time, and the team knew if he was busy and it was a short visit as he kept his coat on. As Martin House managed clusters of children with symptoms that were uncommon in District General Hospitals, expertise grew and became recognized throughout the region and beyond. There was close collaboration with doctors working in other Hospices so that the management of rare symptoms and the use of medication in novel ways was shared. A local Consultant in Adult Palliative Medicine worked part time, including on-call, bringing in her expertise. It has been felt important that any doctor seeing children and young people at Martin House should have knowledge of the Hospice and its capabilities, so out of hours cover has always been from a small group of doctors.

consultant appointment

The local GP, Dr Brady, took a sabbatical from his practice to work full time at Martin House for a period of one year. This allowed continuity of care and the building of strong relationships with families and children. When children were at home then local primary care services could be supported, sometimes by telephone at other times by visits to the home.

The announcement of the possibilities of New Opportunity Funding renewed thoughts about appointing a Consultant. After some delay in agreeing job descriptions and, importantly, the future funding of half the post though the NHS, a Consultant was appointed. There were concerns that this might mean a change in the care offered at Martin House.Would there be more interventions? Would families have to wait for the doctor to say when they could leave as in hospital?

Despite best efforts Rainbow room has not been turned into an Intensive care room, nor does the Hospice own a pulse oximeter! In true multi-professional working, knowledge and thoughts have been exchanged. Hopefully the staff have learned as much from the Consultant as he has learnt from them. There are now sufficient doctors for one to be providing care to the children attending Martin House and one to be visiting those children who need extra support at home, hospital, school or elsewhere. Good links have been established with local Children's Community Nurses so that there can be a rapid response for children and families in need. Weekly visits to the oncology service and the intensive care units ensure that children in hospital who suddenly need help can access services from Martin House quickly.

Freedoms of Palliative care

One success of having a Consultant with a roving brief has been the possibility of reducing hospital admissions, with the alternative options of Martin House and/or being supported at home. In many of the conditions we see at Martin House there comes a time in the child's illness that hospital admission is unlikely to be of any great benefit. Indeed the automatic, often multiple, attempts at inserting intravenous cannula can be more burden than benefit. It is now easy to provide suction and oxygen at home. With the provision of the right antibiotic following the correct culture of specimens in the local hospital, then all the treatments that might be offered by the hospital can be offered elsewhere. Although caring for an ill child at home can be a significant added stress for carers, there is often less stress than having to stay on a ward separated from other dependent children. Local nursing services, continuing care or support within or from Martin House can give families choices.

The recognition that despite all attempts the underlying illness is not amenable to present medical treatment allows the carers to concentrate on the child's present quality of living, rather than continually worrying about what the future may hold. The process of writing a formal care plan and then negotiating this with school, local GP, and hospital allows the family to understand and consider their choices. They should be empowered to regain an element of control.

Parallel Planning

It has been said that palliative care is the management of suffering and uncertainty. Sadly the uncertainty is not about what will happen but when and how. It is surprising how much faith is placed in a doctor's prediction of length of life. Studies have shown that even when estimating the life expectancy for the 'average' child in this situation doctors are more often wrong than right. Chest infections are a common final illness that overwhelms a child. However the child will often suffer many such infections in their lives, meaning that predicting which infection will be the final one is usually impossible. Up to one in three of all children who are admitted to Martin House in what is expected to be their final illness make a partial recovery and are able to go home again. This uncertainty makes planning the future very difficult. Accepting the child for who they are now, despite their illness and knowing that they are as comfortable and happy as they can be provides some basis for managing the future.

Palliative care provides the reassurance that the child will have the care they need and that every effort will be made to keep the child comfortable. The care is holistic, taking into account the whole family. Members of the family are encouraged to consider their needs as well.

Symptom Control

One of the sayings of Cicely Saunders (the founder of the Hospice movement) was, 'there is never nothing that can be done'. This has to be distinguished from the, 'everything must be done' that may be a blind attempt to ignore the future. All treatments have side effects, burdens as well as benefits. In the extreme of the end of life the use of medications has to be personalized. Changes may have to be made quickly, so access to the clinical team must always be available. At such times it may be important to have a plan C up one's sleeve if both plan A and plan B fail to provide the needed relief. Acting with confidence and yet maintaining openness and honesty becomes part of the art of medicine. Recognising that it is a privilege to care for people at such a time ensures that the relationship is one of equals, all contributing to the best care.

A Children's Hospice is a marvellous facility in which to provide care, but does this mean that having a Consultant attached is essential? Hopefully the care team feel they are supported to provide complex care. The close association with families means that relationships are easier to establish. Families have access to specialist palliative care, with more concentration on care than can be provided outside hospital. If the consultant spent more time in a hospital this may improve the quality of palliative care on hospital wards, but good care has traditionally been a strength of paediatrics. With Paediatric Palliative Care only just being a recognised subspecialty there are only likely to be a few specialists in each region for sometime to come. As in adult palliative medicine, close working with hospices is essential, but it would be good to have one Consultant working in hospitals and one outside in each region.

So what has become of the cross young doctor who felt that, 'everything must be done'? There has come recognition that everything that benefits the child must be done, and then there may be a gap that modern medicine struggles to fill. The power of the Hospice means that palliative medicine has become a strong bridge.

Martin House - one doctor's perspective: **Debbie Box**

When I started working at Martin House, I left behind my secure world of hospital paediatrics with its ward rounds, hierarchical medical teams, blood tests, X-rays, outpatient clinics and treatment protocols. This was a bit of a culture shock at the beginning, but my time at Martin House has taught me to be a better doctor. Making a diagnosis became about using my senses, one of the most important being my hearing. Not just for listening through my stethoscope but really listening to the words of the children and their families. Medical input is very individual and there are few protocols. Children with the same diagnosis can have very different experiences and symptoms, and varied responses to medication. Medicines used at Martin House are used in quite different and sometimes unique ways to attempt to control some distressing symptoms. A great deal of time is taken in thinking about different therapeutic measures and a lot of care is taken in explaining approaches to the child and their parents.

At Martin House there are no ward rounds with a list of instructions from the doctor; instead there are requests from the care team on behalf of the child to be seen. For some children and their families Martin House is a refuge from the intrusive world of doctors and tests and hospital routines and our only contact is sitting together at lunch. This is of great value in itself so that if a time comes when there is the need for palliative medicine or terminal care, the doctors have an informal familiarity.

Martin House displays a remarkable model of team work where everyone has a valuable and valued role in the care of the children and young adults. Everyone involved with the hospice is working towards the same goal – to support the children and young people with life limiting illnesses and their families in a very personal, flexible and holistic way. This common goal ensures that wonderful care is given to the children and families, but also provides a nurturing, supportive environment for the staff themselves. I have personally valued the many hugs shared between myself and friends, colleagues, children and families.

Time is a wonderful resource at Martin House. There is no limit to how long we can sit with a child and their family to talk and listen or observe and monitor symptoms, nor a limit on how many times we talk over the same issues. I have had the privileges of sitting with parents whilst their child is dying in their arms and with families after their child has died. I have no pager that will bleep intrusively and the care team will only ask to see me discretely if there is a true emergency. I have also enjoyed being able to have the time to share a lot of happy moments or simply sit with a teenager or a parent having a cup of tea and a chat.

Working at Martin House is a great privilege, and the moments of birth and death are the most intimate of life. My time with some of the children and families is only a short part of their journey but I am honoured to share some of it.

200

clinical psychology

life's interesting twists

Looking back over the twists and turns of my professional life it is interesting to see how I arrived in this newly created post of Consultant Clinical Psychologist at Martin House. With hindsight I can see how my interest in working with seriously ill children and their families was stimulated very early on in my career. One significant incident was when I was working as a young psychologist in a busy academic paediatric department. I met an inspiring teenager with an aggressive and challenging degenerative condition. She was outgoing, caring, strong-willed and vibrant. She had wanted to be a nurse or a doctor but she knew she would not live long enough to do that. As well as working clinically, I was teaching a new programme to medical students at the time and she asked if she could help these young people understand something of what it was like from the inside. It was the start of a very special collaboration, during which we recorded conversations together every six months for the next few years as her condition progressed. Looking back over them it is striking how physically she might have weakened, but emotionally she grew. I still often think of her and her family, from whom I learnt so much. I wonder what she would think of me arriving eventually in this post.

A newly evolving role

There is much variety in this evolving role. I work with the children and young people themselves; I remember one six year old boy who said, 'Every child should have a psychologist to see his feelings.' I also work with the families of children who are very ill or have a life-threatening condition. Often this means the parents and brothers and sisters, but sometimes the wider extended family. Frequently the well brothers and sisters try so hard not to stress further an already over-stretched family that they value greatly the range of group and individual supports that Martin House has put in place for them. On occasions the parents we see are not still together, but they want to come together for their child at this time. Feelings can run high but, for their child's sake, they want to manage the situation as well as they possibly can.

As I am employed by the hospice it means that people can see me directly if they want to. They do not have to be referred to an outside organisation. They know that at this exhausting time they will not have to find the energy to begin from scratch, because they know I work particularly with families who have a very ill child. Their feelings and experiences are not regarded as a problem or abnormal, rather they are respected as an integral part of extraordinary circumstances.

A resource

Different members of a family can end up in very different places, coping in very different ways. Sometimes I work with people individually, sometimes with the whole family. On occasions this is in the hospice, at other times in the community. This is not always in ways that I expected. Last year, for example, I ended up writing a book for parents. It had not been my original plan to do this, but it happened because a pressing concern of so many children with life threatening illnesses is for their parents.

Each member of the care team will provide many aspects of care, from dealing with gastrostomy feeds to organising treasure hunts. Everyone is mindful of the psychological and emotional needs of each child and family alongside the physical challenges of the illness. However, given the nature of the work and the powerful dynamics involved, it is helpful to have someone on hand with a specific psychological background as both a formal and informal resource to staff as well as families. For example, as Kathy Laurie writes in her piece on page 244, the staff at Martin House work hard to be 'both professional and involved.' It is sometimes a hard balance to achieve, and we are aware we do not always get it right, but it is one we strive for. To help with such matters there is supervision, consultation and support available, both individually or in groups. We also have regular clinical meetings where we come together

© Liz Varley

to discuss how we are managing particular situations, reflect on our experiences and behaviour and share good practice.

Adapting existing psychological models

Sometimes my work draws on existing models from psychological literature, other times it is about adapting work on such things as coping strategies and defence mechanisms specifically for this setting. One such example is the role of 'denial'. Denial is considered by many not to be a great way of coping. However, whilst not a good permanent solution, at times I think it is underrated as a useful strategy. It allows a break in which to pause, have a breathing space and take in the multitude of overwhelming emotions, before deciding what the next best step may be.

Sharing knowledge

The families themselves have so much experience and knowledge that another satisfying part of my job is to facilitate them learning from each other. About two years ago we arranged for parents of children with life-threatening conditions to meet regularly to explore some of the many challenges they face, to share expertise born out of their experience and to give some thought to their own needs. The groups have proved very popular. Tommy, a member of the care team, helped get them off the ground and he writes about them below, along with a poem that gives a real flavour of them from one of the mothers, Mavis.

The parents' groups: Tommy Mylod

'The parents group helps parents to come together and talk about how they are feeling at that particular moment in time. Sometimes someone will come and talk to us; for example, about the various available benefits and allowances. Other times we'll share information about a whole range of things, from feed pumps to holidays and insurance. We have lovely lunches provided by Robin. In the afternoons we have relaxing choices: Margaret massaging our heads and hands, Bren doing reflexology, Helen doing arty things with us - I have quite a collection of painted plates at home now. Parents say, 'We really look forward to this day, it helps us say how we are feeling, knowing that other parents understand. We always have a good day. It is a great group.'

I wish we had a tape
when we are at a parent's group
we laugh and talk across the table
we need a Chair good and able
Jan and Tommy sit well there,
we certainly let down our hair with these two in the chair.
Then relax with Margaret's magic massaging heads and hands
with Helen painting tiles and things,
she'll make a Picasso out of you
I hope you understand.
The lunch is something to look forward to,
Our Robin's a dream
and the puddings supreme.

The things we share among one another are very useful
We should know.
If you should need a holiday with useful gadgets at the scene,
or clothing easier to fit, fashionable and comfortable too,
we want our children smart
well dressed as you.

Money troubles do pop up, knowledge too from one another
printed down on paper.
Self help passed on together, a wonderful thing,
A comfort, two holding hands,
You and me can bring.

research and development

I have also been able to put my research skills into practice in the service of the children and families. We now have an active research programme, with local, national and international collaboration. Some is in the planning stages (such as looking at different pain experiences); some is now completed (such as the study of the longitudinal experiences of the siblings of children with life-shortening illnesses). We work hard to disseminate and share the information with professional and lay audiences.

A central tenet of any research at Martin House is that it must always hold in mind the best interests of the children themselves and their families. This is helped by having the involvement of the young people and of parents on our steering groups and also the active encouragement and involvement of the Trustees. Our research also helps inform our expertise as a specialist resource to the wider community and other organisations, whether this be universities, schools or hospitals.

Lessons learnt

To work at Martin House means to work in a place where you never stop learning, whether this be from colleagues, the children or their families. But it is not just about new knowledge, skills and procedures, important as they are, it is also about learning as a human being. So much of what we do these days is about 'doing' rather than 'being'. At the hospice we have people who, as well as being good at doing, are also good at being. As one mother put it, 'When my young son was dying we dozed fitfully next to him in his room at Martin House. I shall never forget how I awoke one night to see a member of the care team just quietly stroking his head. It was so peaceful, I shall always remember her. It was such a comfort to me. I was so utterly exhausted. I drifted back to sleep.'

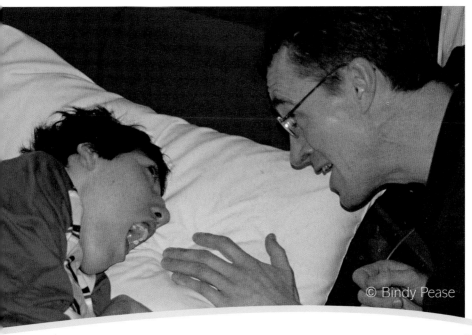

© Bindy Pease

Section Six:

A Rich Tapestry

It has been said that a hospice is a philosophy, not a facility. In the case of Martin House it is also a group of exceptional people, who make up the whole team that delivers that philosophy. Representatives from administration, fundraising and the volunteers who work with them, describe their roles in Chapter 19. The varied contributions of the household team are captured in Chapter 20, alongside some of the other aspects of nurturing and being nurtured. The final chapter, Chapter 21, is written by our chaplain, Mark Clayton, on the role of chaplaincy at Martin House. The book ends with the song that Cathy Ibberson wrote for the 21st birthday year, and in which she expresses something of the space that has evolved, how special that is to be a part of, and what we hope to continue offering in the years to come.

Chapter 19: **administration, fund-raising, volunteers**

The essential backbone

Sue Wigley is PA to the Head of Care, but she has worked in administration in different roles at Martin House for 19 years. She is well placed to provide an overview of the admin team. Robin Wood was the first administrator, and now a Trustee, and he recalls his appointment. Aase Somerscale, present Head of Finance and Administration, acknowledges the generous charity culture in the UK. Her PA, Lorraine Moseley, remembers starting at Martin House, and how on her very first day she was so touched by one of the children that she vividly treasures the memory fourteen years later.

Whenever anyone starts working at the hospice they have an induction period and as part of this they work in all departments. Deborah Hargreave writes about the two days she spent on the care team in her induction period, prior to starting her new post in clinical administration. Sue Kidd is Martin House's receptionist, but this title does not really do justice to what she actually does. She describes something of her varied role, and the contributions of her team of volunteers. Five volunteers working in different roles in the House, (Ursula Turner, Clare Moseley, Janet and Keith Walker and Margaret Evans), share something of what they do and how they have come to be at Martin House.

The second part of this chapter is introduced by Stuart Andrew, another person who fortunately thrives on a role full of variety. Stuart is the fundraising manager and he and his team have the enormous task of not only raising the money that keeps everything going, and working with the many individuals and organisations who so generously donate their time and money, but also informing the wider community about the work of Martin House. Representatives from his team give a flavour of this essential link that fundraising provides between Martin House and the wider community. Amanda Carter, community fund-raiser, talks about one particularly rewarding school visit to a group of 12 year olds; Sheila Clayton, who is Stuart's PA and based in the office, recalls one especially memorable phone call; Jane Horton shares highlights of her job in charge of the lottery; and manager of the Martin House shops, Stephanie Rimmington, shows how no member of a family is safe from getting involved - she has roped in her mother-in-law's talents to write a poem for the shops. This chapter ends with a piece written by Sandy Johnston, and read by her husband, Eugene Johnston, at a Sportsman's Dinner – one of a number of events that they organised to raise money for all the families who need the hospice. They did this in memory of their son Calum Johnston, who died in Martin House when he was fourteen.

Sue Wigley

Martin House was 21 years old in August. It seems incredible that I have been part of the administration team for 19 of those 21 years. In fact the admin team commenced life in a little office in Shoe Shop Cottage in Boston Spa in 1982. To begin with one part time person helped Father Richard with the general correspondence, but the admin and fundraising was dealt with at Shoe Shop Cottage with a few part time people and an administrator. Carolyn Carpenter joined the team full time in 1986 as office supervisor. Lenore Hill, the first Head of Care, joined Carolyn in the September of 1986. Carolyn went on to be one of the major fundraisers and also looked after Trusts until her retirement two years ago. Martin House has always taken pride in the fact that every donation has received a thank you letter. Llewella Parrish joined the administration team in the early days, and for many years typed beautifully written individual thank you letters. The office moved to larger premises, Wits End in the High Street, where they were able to also run a small shop. Despite one or two early major set backs the hard work of this small team enabled

Martin House to open in August 1987, and at this point they moved on site in Martin House. Prior to the opening of Martin House Robin Wood had been appointed Administrator. He and Lenore worked really well together – they had the gift of always knowing so much about each other's team and how it worked. During the course of 1988 Aase Somerscale joined the admin team to look after the accounts. When Robin retired Aase took over the role as head of administration. For the past four years she has had a deputy. This is now Gary Hall. The admin office runs with a very small team, several of whom have worked at Martin House for a long time

When Martin House opened Lenore did not have anybody to do her admin work – this was done in the general office. After three years, Lenore asked if I would be interested in moving from my general role in admin to working for her. It was agreed I would do her work, together with the clinical work of the care team, alongside my general office duties. As the services within Martin House grew it began to be very evident that Lenore needed someone full time. I therefore looked after the office work for Lenore, the doctors and the care team, with the help of my core volunteers, until four years ago. At this time Deborah Hargreave changed from being a volunteer to being appointed to a new clinical admin post, as Martin House continued to expand its services. The admin team continue to be indebted to the volunteers who help us, from answering the telephone to copying up the admission board.

When it was decided to open the teenage unit, we realised that we needed more fundraisers and at this point a larger fundraising team was recruited. As this team grew they had to move off site for a while. They were able to return at the beginning of 2008, after we had managed to extend and convert the store rooms upstairs into offices for them. It makes a real difference to have them back on site. The admin team has always been very much part of the Martin House family and over the last 21 years we have shared many happy times along with the inevitably sad ones. For me it has been a privilege to be PA first to Lenore and now to Sheila O'Leary, who took over from Lenore as Head of Care five years ago.

Robin Wood

I left retirement to apply for the Administrator's post at Martin House and was appointed three months before Martin House opened its doors to its first families; the place was still a muddy building site.

I inherited a small team whose key emphasis was on fund-raising. Fund-raising at that time depended enormously on many hard-working volunteers and a large number of friends groups. (In fact although fund-raising has grown considerably we are blessed that this essential backbone remains.) Being only the second children's hospice we were helped by the fact that we could extend our appeal over the whole country and, indeed, our early families came from all over Great Britain.

Our first families were welcomed in August 1987. From then on the administrative and management needs of the developing hospice were emerging. Happily the Head Nurse, Lenore, and I enjoyed a first class working relationship and two principles dominated our development of the organisation and its management. The first was that the fulfilling of the families needs was the priority and secondly this was to be achieved by a flexible approach to organisation and management. These principles apply to the present day.

We have been well supported over the years by our Trustees. They recognise their responsibilities for care of our finances, for the overall aims of the charity, for the appointment of the two principal officers (ie: Head of Care, and Head of Finance and Administration) and ensuring that they do their jobs. They have left it to the staff to fulfill the executive roles and this has worked well. On my appointment in 1987 I undertook to do three years but instead stayed for seven. A gloriously happy place to work.

Aase Somerscale

Coming from a Scandinavian country where the charity culture is almost non existent Martin House was a whole new, but extremely refreshing, world for me. I was totally overwhelmed by the generosity of the people who unselfishly gave so much to our cause, both in terms of money and time. In my country of origin services such as the ones provided by Martin House do not exist and would not be considered, unless they could be provided fully by government funding. I truly admire the British people for their approach to these matters. Despite the fact that most people would probably agree that such services should be provided by the government, they do not sit back passively, waiting for the government to do something. They are proactive and do something about it. This approach has resulted in many examples of excellent and innovative work, which has been recognised worldwide. Hospice work is one such very good example.

With my private industry background, I was used to focusing on 'the bottom line,' but here in my new job I quickly realised the importance of other key values too; too much focus solely on money could be damaging and certainly should not be the item at the top of the agenda. Although the business aspect is a necessary component in running a charity, there is an awful lot more involved and it is important to recognise that the 'business' can and should be carried out in the background. For Martin House getting it right for the children and their families who rely on our services is paramount and social outcomes are far more important than financial measurements.

I have been totally overwhelmed by the children and families who come to stay at Martin House. Their strength and honesty have inspired me and taught me so much and also enabled me to put things into perspective in my own life. The families and staff have also shown me that, amongst sadness, there is laughter and happiness too and this is reflected in the whole atmosphere of Martin House. I feel extremely privileged to have been given the opportunity of working for Martin House and I shall always treasure the memories of my time here.

Lorraine Moseley

As an office volunteer I was a bit apprehensive on my first day at Martin House. I wasn't sure what to expect. After a welcoming cup of coffee I was whisked off on a tour of the House. Through the bustling lounge area where children were watching television or playing with the various toys scattered about, past the kitchen (lots of busyness here too – scrumptious smells), along a corridor, passing bedrooms and the Jacuzzi room, eventually arriving at the multi-sensory room.

We knocked on the door before peeping in. It was quite dark and a member of the care team was sitting on what looked like a huge padded mat with her arms protectively around a poorly little girl who was lying against her. Together they watched tiny coloured fish bobbing about in a bright, water filled, bubbling tube. I could hear nursery rhymes playing quietly in the background and my eyes then focused on the ceiling, which was a mass of twinkling lights, just like stars in the night sky. As if by magic, coloured shapes appeared and floated serenely about the room. I looked again at the little girl who lay there, looking so contented, quietly enjoying the experience of the room. I wished I had a magic wand….It was a humbling experience.

We crept away and I went back to the office feeling that Martin House was a very special place. I so wanted to help out there in whatever way I could. It had been a huge privilege to have been allowed a little insight into the world of the care team.

A few months later I was exhilarated to be offered a permanent, paid position in the office. That was fourteen years ago and I cannot imagine working anywhere else. I have seen many changes during this period, not least seeing Martin House grow in size when Whitby Lodge opened. There have, of course, been some extremely sad times but there have also been many, many happy and rewarding moments. I have been so fortunate to share these experiences – and that little girl, on my first day, will always be held as one of my most treasured memories.

Deborah Hargreave

'Can you do an early shift in the House and a late in the Lodge with the Team?' Linda asked. Linda Foley, amongst other things, looks after 'Orientation' for all new staff. For someone who was employed to do 9 - 5 in a secretarial job this was a good way for a new starter like me to gain insight into the role of a care team member.

As I recall I was with Jude, who was there to greet me in the House and she asked me if I was happy to help with most things. On that day she was looking after a young lad who sadly was deteriorating quite quickly. His Mum was staying and she too was happy for me to observe and help. In fact, straight away she asked me to cut her son's fingernails because they were very long and she sometimes caught his skin when she attempted to do them and she would rather me try! ..... I filed them! She was a lovely lady and quite a character and on that day was laughing and joking and I sensed relieved to be at Martin House for a well deserved rest. She could forget about running her own house and take advantage of all that Martin House could offer her. This lad needed practically full time attention because of all his medications and personal needs. My day with Jude was non stop; the lad concerned was to have a bath. This involved slings, hoists and equipment I had never encountered.

It made me realise very quickly how drained and tied to the situation carers must be. Constant checking of equipment, looking for small reactions to medications, dealing with fits, never mind the emotional effects of looking after someone 24/7. It was no surprise to me that in quite a few cases the main carer was a single woman either divorced or separated. These people sometimes neither have the time nor energy to enjoy a loving and normal relationship with their partner or time to be just themselves. In addition when there are siblings involved, who gives them the attention they usually crave. My second shift, a late in the Lodge was different again. Caroline took me under her wing. Some of the young people had been having a lie in, after a late (ish) night watching a DVD in the Den or chatting with the night staff and each other. This was a luxury probably they don't have at home. Not because their parents won't let them, but because there are just too many jobs to do and staying up late is just too shattering for their parents. They were having brunch and this late start in the day seemed no different to what my own children did as teenagers. It is no coincidence that sometimes the young people who come in are suffering with a similar condition and they have a special camaraderie. Racing around in wheelchairs was popular on my shift! There was one thing that I remember well. Helping a young man with a fish finger sandwich. This was one of his favourites and because he had no strength in his arms I had to feed him. He was most annoyed that I was not feeding him quickly enough and kept gesturing to tell me so! I was worried in case he was going to choke. Now fish fingers always remind me of him.

I think that looking after teenagers and young people is both challenging and rewarding. These are young people dealing with the usual teenage angst of how they look, physically growing, friendships, sexuality and coping with a disability or condition too. I realised that by them mixing with other young people at Whitby Lodge and chatting to the care team members they could certainly air their views! To me the hub of the place is around the dining room table like many homes.

Reception: Sue Kidd

I first started working in reception in December 2000 and I was a bit of a guinea pig as Martin House had never had a receptionist before. It was quite a sublime time as I seemed to spend the first few weeks buried under teddies and toys as the general public are extremely generous over the Christmas period. Father Christmas came to visit in a helicopter – and seeing the looks on the children's faces was just wonderful. Whilst all this was going on, the fundraising team was busy raising money for a new teenage unit so there was a lot to take in.

Work in reception varies from the typical office type jobs such as dealing with incoming and outgoing post, faxing, photocopying, typing, counting money donated by our very generous supporters, to welcoming the children and families who come to stay and looking after any visitors. This can include, contractors, healthcare professionals, the police, undertakers, taxi drivers, the lovely ladies from Wetherby flowers, and numerous kind members of the public who donate money and gifts to Martin House, to name but a few. We always consider it a very special treat when the children pop into the office to show us their artwork, or to tell us about the songs they have recorded; and we really think we've got it made when we are asked to sample their baking.

Some of the more 'interesting' times have ranged from a telephone conversation with Peggy the Ventriloquist doll, to the day when Martin House was offered some chocolate Advent calendars and six hundred boxes arrived – turning reception into a mini Cadbury's factory, the aroma of chocolate was quite overpowering! My exercise routine at one time included chasing after Holly (Lenore's dog) who used to make a bid for freedom to the village on a regular basis to steal bird food from a neighbour's garden; he had to be dragged back very reluctantly to base camp. Whilst we are on the animal theme, Mary's Farm, with an assortment of wildlife, including several rabbits and Herbie Fudge the goat, visit from time to time, so it is not unusual to find myself carrying a basket containing a guinea pig or two. You just never know what's going to happen next.

I feel very privileged to work at Martin House. It is a very special place, which consists of an amazing team of people including the stirling band of volunteers who give up their free time to support me in the office or go out collecting items (Jobs for the Boys, as they are called). I have only scratched the surface of what comes through the office – needless to say there is never a dull moment!

Ursula Turner

When I retired from my full-time job as a Secretary/PA I wondered how I would fill my time; my husband was still working. Martin House had only just opened so I wrote a letter, giving my background and offering to help in any way they thought I might be useful. I was, in fact, the first office volunteer at Martin House itself and that was 20 years ago now.

Naturally, I started in the office - answering the telephone, counting money from collection boxes, sending out publicity material, etc. I later helped with writing 'thank you' letters and entering information onto the computer when the data base was being established. One morning I was asked if I would be willing to help in the kitchen and over the sixteen or so years since then I have been Robin's Wednesday morning volunteer. I have probably made hundreds of puddings and tray bakes during that time! Working in the kitchen you are very much at the heart of Martin House and a chef like Robin to work with makes it a very special place. His energy and enthusiasm has never changed during all those years and nothing is ever too much trouble for him.

My secretarial experience comes in useful in the afternoon. I work with Sue Wigley in the office, typing letters, putting data onto the computer and helping with other correspondence and general office administration tasks.

When you see what some families are up against and the problems they face, I feel that my day spent at Martin House puts the rest of my week in perspective. It can be a very humbling experience to see how the children and young people cope with their life-limiting illnesses, determined to live life as fully as they can. People often say to me they do not know how I can work at Martin House as they would find it too painful and distrssing. It is sometimes quite difficult to explain to them that although there are inevitably times of great sadness and loss, the general atmosphere is cheerful and positive and the care and support afforded to the children and their families is wonderful and very special.

I am not sure who gets most out of what I do at Martin House, them or me. I thoroughly enjoy being part of the now extensive team of volunteers and really value the many friends I have made since being there. I feel very privileged to be sharing in the work of Martin House in some small way.

Clare Moseley

I have been a volunteer at Martin House for more than sixteen years, and I still vividly remember one of my early experiences here. I'm a keen botanist and was told that the wildflower meadow was worth a look. I walked over to see the ox-eye daisies, buttercups, forget-me-nots, bluebells, clover and vetch, but couldn't find the cowslips I had been told about. As I was wandering around looking down, one of the sisters came out and asked if I had lost something. I told her I had come to find the cowslips, but couldn't find any. 'Well you wont,' she said. 'We've picked them all, as they do make wonderful wine.' She was right, as I know from sampling it later.

Janet and Keith Walker

The first time I heard the name 'Martin House Children's Hospice' mentioned was when I was working at the British Library at Thorp Arch. I was fairly new to the area and living in Wetherby so I had not previously been aware of the huge fund raising effort that had been taking place. A colleague told us that her husband and brother were working at the site and that the first sod had been cut. The department then became very keen to raise funds for the Hospice and over a number of years held numerous fundraising events; our home made cake stall was always very popular.

By the time Martin House was finally completed I had moved to Boston Spa. Before it officially opened, local residents were invited to look round to see what this new building in their community was all about. Keith and I took up the offer and were so impressed by the thought and detail that had gone into the design.

Fifteen years later when we retired we became part of Pauline Bowman's 'Sorting and Stuffing team'. Then Keith became one of the 'Boys,' as in 'Jobs for the Boys', and I joined Sue's team in Reception. Compared to many volunteers our stories are quite recent, but we hope we will be able to collect many more.

Margaret Evans

Time on my hands and a love of children led me to seek out the jewel named Martin House.

Volunteering after many years spent in a very structured career was enticing. I found myself looking forward to my weekly date with Martin House – would it be answering the telephone, counting the cash from collecting boxes or the more familiar clerical work. Whatever, my life became filled with wonder as I grew more and more captivated by the love that surrounds not only the children but all who are fortunate to grace the doors of Martin House. As time went on I realised there were many one-off jobs I could do – washing up at special occasions, sales stalls at planned events or assisting with the clerical work for projects, to name but a few.

Marching into retirement, life's pathway continued to evolve. I added more interests to my already busy life but always made sure I had time for my slot at Martin House. So often I sense an individual struggles to find a means to give time and skills to their 'treasured cause'. By having the framework of Martin House to work within I am safely able to contribute those skills within my available time.

One very vivid memory of my years at Martin House was witnessing a sibling, a very upset little girl in pretty pink pyjamas, on her knees in the hallway, she could hardly speak through tears of her distress. As a member of the care team passed her they enquired quietly, 'Are you able to tell me what is upsetting you?' - through gulps of air the small soul started to explain her grief. The reason matters not but the gentle, touching way the situation was handled I feel epitomises the typical care and thoughtfulness of the staff.

My work there has given life an added perspective and I've discovered skills I never knew existed within me-just because I allowed myself to take a step across the threshold of Martin House to enquire if the time and skills I had could be of use in any small way.

As a privileged volunteer I can only close by saying I often feel embraced with light after a visit to that admirable place named Martin House.

Fundraising: Stuart Andrew

Fundraising has always been a significant part of every day life at Martin House. Even in the very beginning, when Martin House was just a dream, an awful lot of money had to be raised to build the hospice; but it is this fundraising that has helped Martin House become an important part of our community. The link that fundraising provides between the public and Martin House is very important to the organisation and it continues to go from strength to strength.

As the years have moved on and the services at Martin House have been expanded, so too has the need to raise even more funds. Every building has been built by the goodwill and generosity of the public and today the vast majority of the funding of the services we provide comes from donations. It often comes as a shock to most people when they discover that just 7% of the £3.9 million needed each year comes from statutory sources. This leaves Martin House with the huge task of raising the rest. This is why being part of the community and in turn being supported by it is so crucial. Raising this amount of money, every year, is not easy and Martin House has had to adapt and increase its activity to make sure the services are available to the children and families who so urgently need them.

In recent years we have expanded our fundraising team to meet these higher income needs. We have fundraisers who look after corporate, events and community. Their job is to recruit as much support as possible and tell as many people as possible about the work of Martin House. They are all supported by a team who are based back at the office and make sure that everything that needs to be done gets done. Working in fundraising is a very varied job and there is a good deal of flexibility in the team, which is crucial.

Sources of Support

Where does the money and support all come from? In truth, from every part of our community; schools, companies, individuals, events, pubs, social clubs, community groups and so on and so on.

Individuals

Donations from people who give what they can and as often as they can account for a big proportion of our funding. It is so heartening to receive letters from people who want to help and include a donation. What often touches me is how frequently the letters include the line "I wish it could be more". My response is that every penny counts. After all, somebody donating a pound means that we have one less pound to think about. In recent years we have seen an increasing trend in people requesting donations to Martin House rather than receiving a gift for a celebration like a birthday, wedding or anniversary. One of the most touching of these donations came from an eight year old child who asked for money to be given to us rather than buying him birthday presents. He said that the children need Martin House more than he needed toys.

Events

People often donate in other ways by taking part in an event as a runner, walker or parachute jumper. In recent years, the number of events that Martin House takes part in has increased dramatically. Today we can often see the Martin House t-shirts adorned by participants at many famous events. We now have over 300 runners taking part each year in the Great North Run, over 600 in the Leeds 10K and some in far flung parts of the world. The feat of effort that these people put in is incredible and the amount of money they raise is outstanding.

There are people like the man who ran the Great North Run wearing a huge replica of the Angel of the North; or the man who had never run in his life before but who took part in memory of a family member; the father of a child at Martin House who raised thousands and thousands. In the main, however, it is people who just want to help us.

There are of course a host of different events that seem to grow year on year. Our annual Light up a Life appeal is a very special one, when people can buy a light on our Christmas tree and dedicate it to someone special. The special service at the local church which completes the appeal is cherished by all those who attend. The Glitter Ball which is ably organised by the famous Glitter Girls in Harrogate is a glitzy event that now raises in excess of £50,000. Whatever the event is, no matter how large or small, it requires a great deal of organisation and hard work, but so many people do it for us and in the most modest fashion too.

companies

There are a host of companies in the area in which we serve, large, medium and small. We have a great deal of support from this sector, each helping us in many different ways. Some provide funding from the company itself; others encourage their staff to raise money for us. Some organise events, whilst others give us gifts in kind. One company has provided the toilet rolls to us for a number of years free of charge – a very useful donation indeed. This area of fundraising has become very important to us too as many of them like to help a small charity such as ours.

Friends Groups

Friends Groups have an amazing loyalty to Martin House and many of them have existed since before the hospice opened and still work hard for us today. They are often small groups of volunteers who set up these supporter groups in all areas of the county; from Scarborough to Ilkley, Huddersfield to Hull, Otley to Sheffield. Every one of them is busy in their communities arranging events, collections and spreading the "word" of the hospice.

community

All sections of the community help us too. Schools are often calling us to say that they would like to adopt the hospice as their charity of the year. It often starts with a member of the Martin House team visiting the school to talk about our work and then the pupils will go off and come up with different ways of raising money. Social Clubs, community organisations, pubs and clubs are other avenues where money is often raised.

Shops

Over the years Martin House has had a number of shops and currently we have three; Headingley, Skipton and Boston Spa. These are all run by Managers who work extremely hard and are supported by a wonderful band of volunteers who make sure that they get the very best price for all the goods and clothes people donate to us. They also act as a representative of Martin House on the High Street and people learn so much about the organisation from visiting the shops.

I will always recall the amazing story of a man who was walking past one of the shops and decided to go in. He had not heard about Martin House before and asked lots of questions of the manager and volunteers. A few days later he called me to say what he had done and how everyone had been so helpful. He said that he thought Martin House was an amazing charity and that he was the executor of a Will and promptly informed me that he was going to give us a cheque. A few days later a cheque arrived for £42,000! That taught me a valuable lesson on the importance of being visible in the community.

Legacies

People who have supported us over the years often want to continue that support after they have died and kindly make a donation from their will to us. Over the last few years we have seen an increasing proportion of our income come from legacies. This is a very special way of helping to secure our future.

These are just a few examples of where the money comes from. It would be impossible to mention every event or person, because there are literally thousands and thousands. But what is for sure is the fact that without them we would simply cease to exist.

Thank you

It is the community in which we serve that ensures we remain a very important and vital part of that community. A big thank you to everyone who has helped over the last 21 years and our heartfelt thanks for the future.

Amanda Carter

It is our job as fundraisers not just to raise money, but to bring awareness of how difficult life can be for children and young people with a terminal illness and how we can all help each other. Seldom has my job been more rewarding than when I spoke to a particular Year 7 group in a Leeds school.

Standing before 250 twelve year olds can be quite daunting – I know that well as I am a parent of one! So when I visited this particular school in the very early part of my role as a fundraiser I was a little apprehensive to say the least. Sometimes when listening to a talk adolescents can be cheeky and dismissive, or, if you get it wrong, dissolve into tears.

I started my talk telling them about how great Martin House is, how wonderful the care team are, what a fabulous time the kids have. I watched them as their faces changed when they realised how difficult it is to be in a wheelchair, and how much fun you miss when you can't go to the park to 'hang' with your friends. I finished by answering some thoughtful questions from the students. They gave me the regulatory clap and filed out of the hall. Oh well! I thought, that went OK, not great, just OK. Then one boy broke ranks, marched up to me and pushed a hot, sweaty, sticky 10p piece into my hand and said, 'It's all I've got, I've spent my pocket money on sweets in the tuck shop today – but I promise I will raise money for Martin House'. Six months later a cheque for hundreds of pounds arrived from the school. Kids sometimes get a bad name these days with antisocial behaviour, but most are just honest, decent and quite wonderful!

Sheila Clayton

Fundraising receive donations of goods, money, time and sometimes unusual items such as snow.
On Christmas Eve 2007 Martin House was turned into a winter wonderland as ten tonnes of snow was delivered to guarantee the children and families at Martin House a truly white Christmas.

The wonderful day was all down to a very generous businessman, Chris Hopkins and his family. The snow prize was available on auction site ebay and Mr Hopkins was the successful bidder, but rather than keep the snow himself he kindly donated it to Martin House. It was a truly magical day with children building snowmen and having snowball fights, carol singers entertaining the crowds and lots of mince pies to eat.

The publicity this generated for Martin House was worldwide. In the immediate aftermath we received donations from far and wide from people who had seen the story. Even five months on someone informed us they were requesting donations to Martin House in lieu of presents for their daughter's first birthday. When asked why they chose Martin House they said because of the story with the snow at Christmas.

The Martin House Lottery: Jane Horton

Fundraising has many peaks and troughs throughout the year with regard to the volume of money that is donated, and so it was decided to launch our own lottery with a view to having some regular income.
The lottery was launched in June 2005 on a very warm and sunny day; we had many people attending, together with a very colourful hot air balloon. (The picture at the start of this chapter.)

The best part of my job is ringing the top three prize winners every Friday to tell them their good fortune. The reaction varies from person to person, some are very quiet and embarrassed, some are very loud and excited and occasionally we do get some tears. We have been advised that the winnings have paid for, or been put towards, a fridge, a wedding dress, car parts, a holiday in Australia and a pony called Storm. We have also received some very generous donations from our winners for which we are most grateful.

Martin House Shops: Jackie Rimmington

Martin House would like to ask
If you would really be so kind,
To search through all your wardrobes
And see what you can find,
Coats, skirts, or trousers anything like that,
Belts and bags and shoes, perhaps an unused hat,
Toys are always needed and books and jigsaws too,
Any unwanted Christmas gifts
We would be glad to take from you
For our shop in Boston Spa (+ Leeds and Skipton too).
We have room for so much more
And we should be so grateful if you would bring it to our door.

A Sportman's Dinner for Martin House:
Sandy and Eugene Johnston

Before Calum became ill our family had no experience of the hospice movement. Martin House came to our rescue at the lowest point in our lives. For Calum it provided peace and calm and dignity after the turmoil of several weeks in hospital, for our family it provided practical support at a time when we needed it most. We moved in and had our meals cooked, our clothes washed – indeed our every need was taken care of so that we could concentrate on what was important to us at that time, spending time with Calum. They continued to care for him after he died. This was enormously important too. We were able to take him into what they call the 'little room,' which is a special cold bedroom where we could leave him and go to see him whenever we wanted. We were able to decorate it with his posters and personal things and play his music, but it also meant that his friends and family could go and visit him to say goodbye. Martin House still provides emotional support for our family. We realise now the importance of such a place.

It costs well over £3m a year to run and 93% of that money has to be provided through fundraising. Calum's story has inspired so many people; we have been overwhelmed by the response. There has been fundraising from organisations such as our schools, the Scouts and the rugby club; individuals too numerous to mention have found imaginative ways to raise money from long distance cycle rides to immersing themselves in the sea on Boxing Day, to holding bun sales and sky diving; concerts have been held and miles have been run, others volunteer to help, and supporting all these are those of you who are willing to dig deep and provide sponsorship. On behalf of the Martin House families - thank you.

© Bryony Wright

Being Nurtured

So much of Martin House is about nurturing. Over the twenty one years Hazel Clough has both seen and given a lot of nurturing. She is well positioned to introduce some of the nurturing that goes on quietly at Martin House on a daily basis. Martin House's own celebrity chef, Robin Wraith, and one of his long-serving kitchen volunteers, Carol Spratt (known to many for her seemingly never ending supply of cakes and tray bakes) include two favourite recipes. Olive Young, one of the housekeepers, is also a talented artist and she has contributed her colourful sketch of the team of housekeepers, Angie Birch, Dot Allen and Lynda Roberts. Her artistic skills have also found their way into the mural that her daughter, Donna Young, is creating for the hot tub room. Pam Rogerson, a member of the care team, writes about care for the carers. Peter Dykes, in his poem, captures a recipe for Lenore's 'everlasting pie'. In Gillian Crosby's contribution we see the important and evolving part played by the gardens. Chapter 20 ends with nurturing gifts to the team at Martin House, from two people who have seen their work at close quarters. The first is from Dr Barry Wright, who provided a weekly staff support group over 15 years, and the second is from a mother, Kathy Lawrie, who writes an open letter to the staff.

The importance of being nurtured: Hazel Clough

Before Martin House welcomed the first families in August 1987 it held one or two general open days to thank the many people who had helped get it off the ground. We were all so proud of the beautiful buildings and the carefully chosen furnishings. Some visitors expressed their surprise that it was more like a hotel than a hospital. Although we had not quite expected these comments, with hindsight they were very perceptive. How many nights would parents have dozed in a chair beside the hospital bed of their child. How often did they juggle the care of their poorly child with that of their other children. When do they get the chance to be all together in the same place at the same time, to have an uninterrupted night's sleep, or to sit down and eat a meal together. We wanted to be able to offer these things to the families who were to come to stay with us. So alongside finding the right kind of people to be a part of the team at Martin House, a beautiful environment has been important from the start. There are extra beds in the children's rooms, but there is also spacious, separate parent accommodation if families want it. It is comfortable and kept spotlessly clean by our team of dedicated housekeepers. Providing the families with a comfortable room where they can rest for a while and spend time with each other goes some way towards helping them to find the energy for their return home. Many parents simply find the luxury of a long soak in the bath an enormous treat and a great way to relax, knowing that their children are being cared for by the team.

We are fortunate in having beautiful gardens which, thanks to our maintenance men and a dedicated band of garden volunteers, provide us with a visual treat throughout the seasons. There is lots of space for the children to get some fresh air and to play, and exciting corners for all to explore, including those children who use wheelchairs. Such a lot of thought has gone into the design of the gardens. It is possible to take long walks seemingly away from everything,

to spend time on the garden swing in the 'secret' garden, or to enjoy just being together as a family. When the weather allows we have wonderful barbecues enjoying the sunshine, or in a shady spot beneath one of the trees.

Food is a very important part of the day at Martin House and for many of the children and families who come, Robin our chef remains the single most important member of our team. Having nourishing meals provided each day also helps the families to feel rested and refreshed, and is a vital part of the care we offer. Robin believes that the mealtimes allow opportunities for families to sit down together, to meet and share with others and to relax and unwind. Most of all perhaps, simply not having to think about the preparation of a meal can be a real treat for some.

Robin Wraith

Robin is that very same young man that Lenore talks about appointing as chef in Chapter 5. He can turn his hand to anything, from helping children prepare their own individual pizzas to events for hundreds. A vivid memory of one mother whose child had died on Christmas Eve, was how he had time to play leisurely with her other children and their new toys on Christmas morning at the same time as apparently effortlessly preparing Christmas dinner for everyone else.

This is Robin's recipe for a favourite cake from the Martin House kitchen.

Mayonnaise Cake
10 oz SR flour (sifted)
1 teaspoon baking powder
4 tablespoons cocoa
1 teaspoon vanilla essence
8 oz caster sugar
7 oz mayonnaise
8 fl oz boiling water

ICING
4 teaspoons instant coffee
4 tablespoons cocoa
4 tablespoons hot water
6 oz margarine
1 lb icing sugar (sifted)

Mix together flour, sugar, baking powder and mayonnaise. Dissolve cocoa in the hot water. Stir into mixture with vanilla essence. Turn into greased and lined tins. Bake at Mark 4,180C, 350F for approx 35 mins. Cool in tins before removing. For the icing, dissolve cocoa and coffee in the hot water. Cream margarine and icing sugar and beat in the liquid. Spread over the top and sides and sandwich cakes together.

Carol Spratt

Carol has been involved with fund-raising for Martin House since before it opened, and has been one of Robin's volunteers for twenty-one years. She always seems to remember just which child and family likes which cake. Here she shares the recipe for a chocolate cake that is the favourite of a discerning young man from the Lodge and which she always makes when he comes to stay.

Chocolate cake
8 oz margarine
8 oz cater sugar
8 oz self raising flour

2 teaspoons baking powder
1oz cocoa
4 eggs

Sift flour, baking powder and cocoa into large bowl. Simply add all other ingredients and whisk with an electric hand whisk until thoroughly combined. Add two teaspoons warm water to make dropping consistency. Line two cake tins. Divide mixture between two tins. Bake 30 mins at gas mark 3, 325F , 170C. Turn out when cool. Sandwich together with whipped cream and strawberry jam. Ice with chocolate icing and grated chocolate. Enjoy.

The housekeeping team

© Olive Young

237

New hot tub mural

© Donna Young

Pam Rogerson

As part of the philosophy of Martin House is to care for the whole family, in the last few years some parents have asked us about various complementary therapies for themselves. We do not offer this formally but we have a few members of the team who are qualified in different therapies including, aromatherapy, reflexology and reiki. If anyone in a family wants to try them we can sometimes provide a taster at some point during their stay.

I saw one mum for a Reiki session. During the session I could tell that she was drained and exhausted.. She confirmed that not only was she caring for her son who was very ill, but she was also giving a lot of emotional support to her friends. I pointed out that it was also important to care for herself so that she had enough energy to care for the others in her life. The next time I saw her she told me that she had started trying to have one hour a day for herself. She said she was feeling so much better with this seemingly small change; better able to cope with events in her life and having more energy. How amazing that something so simple as taking an hour out of your day and doing something for yourself could have such a dramatic effect. I am not sure whether it was the Reiki that helped her to do this, being given the 'permission' to give some time to herself or something that I had said that had allowed her to carry it out. This isn't actually important, but to see the results was very rewarding.

Lenore's Everlasting Pie: Peter Dykes

I was asked to write a favourite recipe to put into your book
Either one to feed the eyes and mind or just to wish good luck
I said I don't do domestics so baking 's out of touch
So I stole a recipe you've perfected
For a pie of which you can't get too much.

Ingredients

1 pinch of reality
1 cupful of a dream
1 full heart
I smile
A passion
1 child (any size will do)
Mix with liquid sunshine

Allow blending together in any way you prefer
Choose any mould available, from the outcome it will not deter
Keep checking that you have mixed it well if not adjust the mix
Add some personality, there are no special tricks

Watch the product start to grow and you can savour it for days
Can be enjoyed at anytime in Oh so many ways
You'll never run out of mixture or the need to bake these cakes
You can see the nourishment it gives and the difference it makes

So enjoy this little recipe it will always keep you full
A diet 's out of the question for a food that is never boring, bland or dull

Head Garden Volunteer: Gillian Crosby

I came to voluntary work from a background of working in the Electricty supply industry for 37 years in management roles in the retail sector. As retirement loomed my thoughts went to how I would like to spend my time, having worked full time all my adult life. I decided I would like to do some voluntary work. One day I was in the village of Boston Spa and saw a poster in the Martin House shop window asking for garden volunteers; absolutely perfect, I could combine my passion for gardening and my voluntary work all in one.

Lenore Hill, the then Head of Care, became my mentor and I became her head gardener. The relationship worked well; she encouraged me, gave me inspiration and on many occasions gave me my head on projects to significantly change areas of our six acre garden. Lenore's principals and values were the very essence of what created the Martin House you see today. I miss her dearly.

The first major change was to alter the garden at the entrance to the House. My project was to clear a heavily planted shrub garden at the entrance and turn it into a Courtyard garden, to provide an area for the parents and families to linger a while, sit on the garden seat and have time to let the warm blanket of Martin House surround them before they entered the House. I applied for and won a Millenium Award, which was available for hospice volunteers. I think this is still my favourite part of the garden. (Now matured, this area that Gillian talks about is shown in the photograph at the start of Section 2.)

It is now eleven years since I became the head garden volunteer at Martin House; much has changed in these past years, the staff within the House, the addition of Whitby lodge, the volunteers and of course the garden. The six acre garden site has moved on within the last decade, trying to meet the growing needs of the children and their families. It was early on in my career at Martin House that we introduced the hanging baskets to the colonnaded walk to the entrance to the House (shown at the start of Chapter 1); this feature continues to give pleasure to all who visit us from June to October. Our special thanks go to Alan Wilcock and his team at Riverside Nurseries who lovingly make them for us each year.

The old willow walk which meandered through the parkland has gone, it was beyond refurbishment and had become impossible for wheelchair access and in the summer had become the home of wasps. It has now been replaced with a trellis structure with plants growing along its complete length and of course you can manoeuvre your way securely throughout its entire length. Tiger Bridge remains magnificent overlooking the whole site. (It can be seen at the start of Chapter 18.) The children's gardens, which reflect the colours of the rainbow, continue to be pleasant areas outside each of the bedrooms in the House. I designed and we installed a new sensory garden in 2004. This garden is often used by our children and families alike, and the floor mosaics and animal bricks in the raised brick beds form a good hide and seek project for the care team to do with the children; the plants are at the right height to smell, feel and touch. I think this is my second favourite area of the garden.

The Whitby Lodge garden has now acquired maturity and provides a stunning background to the young people's own private space. The requirements for this area were outlined by the very people who were to use this addition to Martin House. I remember that the two most important features were for a modern fountain and for white flowers which could be easily seen in the twilight and evening hours, this being their special time of day.

Three years ago the garden volunteers were invited by the care team to take part in the 'Time 4 Us' programme, this involves three meetings during the year. Our part was to include a gardening feature for the siblings to be included in their fun day of activities at Martin House. By this time I am an avid allotment holder, so it seemed the perfect project to have with the children to plant and grow vegetables with them. (A picture is on page 161) We are now in our third year and the children seem to love it - to plant, harvest and eat the vegetables, to sow the seeds for flowers and then watch them grow; so all is going well.

We are constantly given help and support by outside organisations in our endeavours to provide a pleasant and peaceful environment for our children and families. Over the years I have been given help from many other volunteers; Jim Fletcher and I made a good team, often referred to as little and large, me being five foot nothing and Jim being six foot four – very handy for those tall jobs! But I must mention my two current garden volunteers, Janet Coleman and Mona Benson who come week in and week out and tackle any job presented to them. They love coming and they love making a difference to the lives of the people who come to Martin House. For my part it is the children and families of Martin House who keep me motivated and keep me coming back for more.

A Sense of Belonging: Barry Wright

There is something about Martin House that pulls at the heart strings, gives a sense of calm, a wholesome feeling that stands it out as a place with a soul. For anyone who has spent any time at Martin House there is a keen sense of being accepted, nurtured, recharged. I had the privilege to meet the staff on a weekly basis between 1990 and 2005 to facilitate a Staff Support Group, and even now when I return I still have a very keen sense of belonging. I know that many families and staff members feel the same.

It is easy to say, but it really is true that Martin House is a rather special place. What makes it so special is more difficult to define, because it cannot be pinned down to any one thing. The children and their siblings, of course. Every one of them a bundle of personality. Every one of them able to flourish and express themselves at Martin House. Each of the families able to lay out their fears and hopes.

Many staff say that socially people often remark, "How can you work at a Children's Hospice? I could never work there!", and yet this misses the point. It sees children in the wrong light as a dying child and nothing else. Martin House is not at all like that. Martin House is full of fun and laughter and games and joshing. It allows children to be themselves again. It works hard to get rid of nasty symptoms like pain and moves them out of the way. It works hard to let children express themselves and be who they are, and it works hard to help families contain their understandable fears and angers and find the laughter, the cuddles, the shared mealtimes, the fun, the sense of family and respect for all the people in it. Martin House does not have all the answers, but it does create an ethos and an atmosphere of respect and care and fun where any potential answers may be found, and where resilience can grow.

What other things contribute to this wonderful atmosphere? The vision and passion of Lenore Hill who created a home and not a Ward, who was able to see way past the need for physical cares and understand that families needed nurturing, love, care, and emotional, psychological and social support. Lenore was a person who would stand up against silly bureaucratic rules and protect the needs of the family to have a family life. She brought home and family to Martin House. Everyone at Martin House has carried this legacy on with a calm passion.

In Staff Support Meetings over many years the Care Team have had the opportunity to discuss anything difficult that they are going through. Throughout these meetings they have shown their sense of ownership for the ethos of Martin House. They have shown their beliefs that the families are central to their thinking, that children are complete human beings (they are far more than the illness they have), that fun and humour are uplifting, that everyone is unique and that it is a privilege to get alongside a family. Staff support has shown me over the years how much the staff also have that keen sense of belonging that is one of the important ingredients that makes Martin House a place with a soul. Boy what soul!

To the Staff

I wonder if you know how much difference you make.

I remember how you improved my parenting for a start. I used to watch how you were with my children, how you enjoyed them, how often you said 'Yes!' Martin House is such a 'yes' place. And I thought, 'I can take some of that home'. It wasn't the quantity of attention I could replicate –there was only one of me – but the quality. When you played with the children, you weren't just keeping them occupied; you were really playing, giving it and them your full attention. I learned from that.

You gave me your full attention too. I know that good listening is part of your everyday working life. So you might forget what a rare and valuable thing it really is. I won't forget being listened to-without fear of being criticised or judged or told what to do.When I look back, I don't remember many words; but I do remember the quality of your attention and how that made me feel about myself. Don't ever think that you're 'just' listening.

Then there's the extra mile. There's this myth that you can't be professional and involved- what's that about then? I've seen and experienced some of the best professional care ever at Martin House. I've also seen you laugh and cry with us, seen you carrying your own pain that comes with getting close. You dare to risk being vulnerable and open to what the children especially have to give. That is the extra mile. It is much easier to be just on the giving end, much safer. But when you receive from the children, you enable them to make a contribution to life at Martin House, to make a difference to you. Receiving like that costs more than giving.

There is much more of course, but not the room to say it. I hope you know that you made a very great difference in our lives. I try to take what I learned from you now and offer it to others.

You're still making a difference.

Kathy Lawrie.

chaplaincy

Introduction

For at least one of my colleagues the mention of chaplaincy conjures up childhood memories of religious people in a religious school repeatedly making the sign of the cross. For others it is associated with the nuns who used to live alongside Martin House, and were instantly identified by the religious habits they wore. Fortunately the friends I work with rarely mention to me any disappointment they may feel that I am neither a priest nor a nun, or that I am not immediately recognisable as a chaplain!

Chaplaincy at Martin House nevertheless continues in the tradition of pastoral and spiritual care which was established by Richard Seed and continued by the sisters and Janet Kendal before me. It is a focus of, and resource for, this dimension of care which is offered by the whole team, and is worked out in a partnership alongside and together with them.

Listening

Many of the team will say that they came to Martin House so that they could have more time with children, young people and the families who come, and part of this is about having time to listen and simply be with them. Everyone here is involved in listening, and this is one focus of the chaplaincy role - although it can be a fine line between being around to listen and looking like you have nothing to do and need a job!

The experience of parents, children, siblings, teenagers and grand parents is characterised by different kinds of loss at different stages of their journey, and one of the challenges we face is listening out for those sometimes fleeting occasions in the midst of everyday activities when they may wish to talk about this.

In his talks and booklets, Ted Bowman has shown how a significant aspect of this is about the loss of dreams. One example of this occurred one day when a story we told about dreams prompted one teenager to share a little about her dreams of walking again now that she was confined to her wheelchair. Another example occurred during a visit I made to a teenager with a life-threatening condition, whose brother had recently died. He showed me a poster he had on his bedroom wall, which had a photo of a climber on a rock-face, accompanied by the words, 'Don't let your fears stand in the way of your dreams.' Listening to him was about responding to his hopes of living a normal life in spite of his illness.

Listening enables people to tell their story, and stories can be one way in which young people express themselves and their spirit, or spirituality. Towards the end of his life, one young man began to dictate stories to the care team and other carers, which he then asked his dad to read to him. These stories gathered together and integrated various memorable activities from his life, as well as quirky details about how his dad sometimes hadn't quite got his care right. Consequently this made for some amusing as well as healing times between them when the stories were read together.

The Chapel

There is much in the environment of Martin House that confers dignity and significance to people, and expresses the philosophy of palliative care which is based on caring for the human spirit as well as the body and mind. This is illustrated by the architect's design of the house on the model of a harbour or port in a storm. It is also evident in the woodland chapel, which uses the idea of a boundary wall beyond which there is an uncluttered, peaceful place, and a quiet garden - which may resonate for some as an image of life beyond the boundary of our deaths.

Chaplaincy here involves a broad approach which aims to honour both the Christian origins from which the hospice has grown and the real variety of beliefs and outlooks on life which families bring. This means that the chapel is used in an interesting variety of ways, ranging from some which are broadly therapeutic to others which are more recognisably connected with faith, or faiths.

Parents from the parents' group have come here to relax and talk while having some hand massage, while in the summer we have often simply got together with the younger children for some singing and story-telling. Christian services take place here, including christenings, and celebrations of Christmas which can be moving, entertaining and surprising in true Martin House fashion!

Gradually we have also gathered artefacts here from different faiths to reflect the diversity of families using us, and some of these have been provided by representatives of these communities with whom we have growing friendships. Sometimes the chapel has been a place where we have caught glimpses of children explaining their different traditions to each other in a very natural, friendly way far removed from the hostility often reported in the press!

Remembrance

If spirituality is about the relationship between our inner and outer selves, it is also about the relationships, or 'continuing bonds,' we have with those who have died. Chaplaincy here also involves one hand among many in co-ordinating the day we have each year when we invite bereaved families from the last two years to join us and remember their children together. True to form, the 'service' or time we have for remembering is set in the context of lots of food, play and chat. Through poetry, photographs and music, lighting candles and giving spring-flowering bulbs to the families, we hope to create a space in which they can grieve, remember and also celebrate the lives of their children.

One reading which has proved significant has been a picture of grieving from the tradition of the native American Indian people. It tells how an Indian man will express the wound of his grief by making a deep wound in a tree, which then becomes a focus for his grief. He returns to it when he needs to, so as to be quiet or weep or remember his loved one who has died. As time goes by, the wound in the tree begins to heal, and it continues to grow. For the man, too, the mark remains, and he will never be the same, but he also continues to grow. This reading describes a ritual of the kind that can help sustain people through such times, and of which the day of remembrance is an example.

In various ways at Martin House there are opportunities for memory-making and ritual, which enable families to continue expressing their love and care for their child after they have died. One example is the way in which we make hand or footprints to cherish their memory. Another is the way in which they may wish to light candles or use the memory tree in the chapel.

We have gathered a file of readings for funerals as a resource for families, and have increasingly encouraged them to involve local priests or ministers in funerals, in order to build links within their local communities and find ongoing support beyond Martin House.

HOPe

Writings on palliative care invariably emphasise the significance of hope, and chaplaincy here involves a recognition of this.

Our service of thanksgiving for the twenty first birthday of Martin House in York Minster aimed to encompass this. (Cathy Ibberson, music therapist, captures something of the atmosphere and space that has evolved at Martin House in the song she wrote for the occasion, which is included at the end of this chapter and which brings the book to a close.) The service also included Val Hewison's poem, "Tomorrow came today," which describes how her daughter's death removed all the colour from her world. At the same time, set alongside this was a reading describing the gifts of children and young people, and how they enrich our lives. Towards the end of the service, there was another poem, which encourages us to nourish, nurture and grow hope, "colourful as a rainbow, like a butterfly – fragile yet flying high."

Martin House has been a place of hope for many families, in that it has helped them discover that, with the right kind of help, they can get through one of the most painful of experiences, the death of one's child. There is a sense then that, "each life is indeed a gift, no matter how short, no matter how fragile. Each life is indeed a gift, to be held in our hearts forever."

common Threads

A feature of the images which have been used about Martin House such as the tapestry, rainbow and harbour is that they bring different threads, colours and journeys respectively together into one. In this way they all capture the essential essence of Martin House. Along with other roles here, and often in partnership with them, chaplaincy is also about finding common threads, and affirming the whole of the hospice.

Martin House Twenty-First birthday Song:

Cathy Ibberson

1. A humble beginning, a dream with uncertain tomorrows
   Finding the people, trying to get it right for everyone.
   Who could know where time would lead us
   There is nowhere quite the same
   So here we stand to reflect on this day...

   And we hope,

   This is a place where you can rest,
   Lay down your burdens on our shoulders for a while,
   We will strive to be beside you, at home and as our guests,
   This is a place where you can rest.

2. Not just a building, But a space with a soul
   Seasons turning, we are touched we are changed
   Who could know the courage and despair
   Amidst the tenderness and care,
   All the moments so precious with your children

   And we hope

   This is a place where you have time,
   To play and relax, paint a picture and sing a rhyme,
   Have food laid out before you, leave the daily toil with us,
   This is a place where you have time.

3. (Instrumental)

   And we hope,

   This is a place where you can smile,
   Share your emotions, with us for a while,
   (share the wonder of your children)
   Let tears and laughter be okay, be not afraid to say,
   This is a place for you to smile....

Contributors

Jan Aldridge
Stuart Andrew
Jo Ansty
Sarah Aspinall
Cliff Bailey
Ginny Barker
Christian Bedford
Judy Blair
David Bond
Callum Borders
Ted Bowman
Debbie Box
Hazel Brown
Sam Browning
Jill Carr
Tony Carr
Amanda Carter
Derek Chapman
Mark Clayton
Hilary Clayton
Sheila Clayton
Lesley Clements
Michael Clements
Hazel Clough
Gillian Crosby
Ann Douglas
Bob Drought
Peter Dykes
Margaret Evans
Linda Foley
Georgina Gadsby
Kay Gadsby
Michael Gilroy
Deborah Hargreave
Claire Hayes

Sue Hayes
Linda Hedley
Lenore Hill
Jane Horton
Lucy Hosany
Cathy Ibberson
Caroline Illingworth
Judith Isayenkova
Elaine Johnson
Sandy Johnston
Jo Keeling
Janet Kendall
Val Kennedy
Sue Kidd
Cath Knowles
Kathy Lawrie
Olivia Lindley
Pam Lineham
Amy Livesey
Jude Lyon
Anthony McFadden
Katie McFadden
Mike Miller
Lorraine Moseley
Clare Mosley
Bernadette Murray
Tommy Mylod
Mary Newbegin
Louise O'Leary
Sheila O'Leary
Denise Quinn
Chris Rattray
Mavis Rawson-Chad
Jackie Rimmington
Colin Rogers
Pam Rogerson

Helen Scouller
Richard Seed
Justin Sinclair
Stacey Sinclair
Pam Smith
Aase Somerscale
Carol Spratt
J Spratt
Carol Sykes
Louise Taylor
Adam Tempest
Andrea Topp
Ursula Turner
Janet Walker
Keith Walker
Alison Ward
Wil Warren
Sue Wigley
Michael Wildblood
Jenny Wilkinson
Robin Wood
Robin Wraith
Louise Wray
Barry Wright
Olive Young

Photographers

Nudrat Afza
Paul Carter
Jane Horton
Bindy Pease
Liz Varley
Bryony Wright